Rock Trails

Scottish
Highlands

Paul Gannon

Pesda Press LTD   www.pesdapress.com

Cover Photo: Arkle

First published in Great Britain 2012 by Pesda Press
Tan y Coed Canol
Ceunant
Caernarfon
Gwynedd
LL55 4RN

Mapping contains Ordnance Survey data © Crown copyright and database right 2012

Inside cover road maps based on Ordnance Survey MiniScale®
under Open Government Licence v1.0.

ISBN: 978-1-906095-38-3

Printed and bound in Poland. www.polskabook.co.uk

To the
memory of
Catherine Lowe
and
Mackie Swanson

Ben Nevis from Aonach Beag

Contents

Introduction

The Scottish Highlands are home to Britain's most spectacular mountain scenery. The stark hills, fearful crags, glorious glens and sparkling lochans make for a wide range of landscapes and have attracted generations of landscape lovers, hillwalkers and mountaineers of all description.

This book is intended to help those who adore this landscape to gain an insight into the geological forces that have shaped it. My aim is to explain, in clear straightforward language, why the basic ingredients of hill and glen are able to produce such a remarkably rich mix of landscape types. The mountains and valleys have a fascinating geological history; it is my aim in this book to delve into that history and extract a narrative that is accessible to the ordinary hillwalker and mountaineer. It is a fascinating story which I hope will open your eyes to seeing the landscape in new and more intimate ways.

Photo 0.1

The deeply eroded ancient landscape of northwest Scotland: Cul Mor (right), Canisp (centre) and Suilven (left) seen from Stac Pollaidh. The low ground rocks are up to 3 billion years old.

The book is divided into two parts. The first tells the story of how the rocks were created and shaped by the gross forces of plate tectonics, colliding continents, volcanoes, mountain-building and glaciation. We look back over thousands of millions of years to discover some of the world's oldest rocks in the northwest of the Highlands. We also dig into less ancient geological history, seeking scenic evidence of the powerful glaciers that carved out the present-day landscape in the fairly recent past just a few thousand years ago.

The second part of the book describes 18 recommended walks with a variety of geological features set among consistently fantastic views. The walks are widely spread, encompassing the isolated peaks of Sutherland in the far northwest, the rolling granite massif of the Cairngorms in the east, the haunting beauty of the Ardnamurchan peninsula in the west and a select choice from the vast range of stunning mountains in the central and southern Highlands.

Photo 0.2 |

The intensely deformed rocks of the Grampian Highlands: the Grey Corries seen from Aonach Mor. The rocks date from around 500 million years ago.

The book is limited to the Highlands so it does not cover the equally amazing geology and stunning scenery of the Scottish islands nor the varied landscapes to the south of the key geological feature known as the 'Highlands Boundary Fault' (see Chapter 1). This geographic limitation is logistically essential; to cover the geology of all these areas as well as the Highlands would have demanded either a much bigger book or have meant that less-than-adequate space could be devoted to the mountains of the Highlands.

I have written about what you can see around you as you walk the hills and glens. There is no need to carry any special geological tools such as a hammer or hand lens; it is also unnecessary to take samples back to the laboratory and subject them to various indignities in order to analyse them. I point instead to often quite conspicuous features in the rocks and the overall shape of the terrain in 'reading' the present-day landscape.

While geology is a fascinating subject, it is also a science and relies on a complex scientific terminology. My aim has been to minimise the use of jargon and make the processes that have shaped the landscape comprehensible to the average reader. This has meant some simplification of the jargon and a pruning of the detail. All the same, we will have to deal with a minimal set of terms such as 'plate tectonics', 'plastic deformation', 'magma', 'moraines' and the like.

Photo 0.3 │ Eigg (right) and Rum (left) seen from Ardnamurchan;
these volcanic rocks date from 60 million years ago.

When I first use a piece of jargon I have put it in quote marks (for example, 'continental plate'). Many of these terms are defined in the Glossary, but I have sometimes assumed that the meaning of a term is obvious from the context in which it appears.

While reading the book, the reader may well find it useful to have some maps of the areas covered to hand. This gives a good appreciation of the topographical structure of the landscape features under discussion. It also helps with locating places mentioned in the text (with the help of the list of grid references for all local places found at the back of the book).

Given the considerable area covered by the Highlands, a highly cost-effective and practical approach is to buy the computer-based version of the Ordnance Survey's 1:50,000 maps for the whole of Britain. At the time of writing (early 2012) this could be obtained for less than £70; online versions are also becoming available quite cheaply. Maps are discussed further in the section 'About the Walks'.

Photo 0.4 | Binnein Mor

CHAPTER 1

Before Scotland

A good place to start our look at the geology and scenery of the Scottish Highlands is atop the low prominence know as Conic Hill, found towards the southern end of Loch Lomond, near Balmaha, on its eastern shore. From the western end of the summit area, a line of islands can be seen running across the widest part of Loch Lomond, clearly a continuation of the geological structure of Conic Hill (see Photo 1.1).

Photo 1.1 |
Conic Hill and the line of islands representing the Highland Boundary Fault, which crosses Loch Lomond here.

Conic Hill and the line of islands are the surface expression of what geologists call the 'Highland Boundary Fault'. This major 'fault' (a crack in the earth's crust) is the line of demarcation between Lowland Scotland and Highland Scotland. This boundary is not only of great historical, cultural and economic significance, but also of major geological importance.

Looking roughly to the southwest, the fault is easily traced running across the loch to the southwest as the chain of islands and as noticeably higher ground on the far side of the loch.

Turn around 180 degrees and look roughly to the northeast; a distinct line can be seen separating the higher and lower land, forming what geologists call an 'escarpment' (a sharp slope).

To the north of the escarpment and the string of islands there lies a mass of hills and glens which we know as the Scottish Highlands, running all the way from here to the north coast. Only a small sample of the hills are visible from this viewpoint, which is not surprising given the distances involved. It is all too easy to underestimate just how large the Highlands are. The distance between the most southerly of the Munros, Ben Lomond, and the most northerly, Ben Hope, is the same as that between Conic Hill and the Wrekin, near Chester.

Photo 1.2 | View of the steep scarp slope on Ben Hope, seen from the summit ridge.

Photo 1.3 | View from Ben Lomond, the southernmost of the Munros.

The rocks that make up the mountains and valleys of the Highlands have been created over an incomprehensibly long period of time. Out on the hills, you can come across rocks that were created at any time between a mind-blowing 3 billion years ago and a simply ungraspable 60 million years ago. Since being created, the bulk of the rocks have been heated, compressed, stretched, cracked, folded and buckled; some of the older rocks have suffered such treatment several times over.

The result is a glorious variety of mountain scenery from the immensely ancient landscape of Sutherland in the northwest (see Photo 1.4) to the lusciously pretty hills around Loch Lomond (see Photo 1.3) and much more in between. We will explore the origins of the rocks, looking at their compression and deformation while being piled up into mountains and at how the different rock types and differing geological histories produce the stunning variety of mountain scenery lying to the north of the line of hills marking the position of the Highland Boundary Fault.

Photo 1.4 | Three-billion-year-old gneiss forming the gnarly landscape of the northwest Highlands near Loch Laxford; Ben Stack in centre distance.

The earth is estimated to be just over 4.5 billion years old. We can skip the first 500 million years or so of the earth's life and start our story around 4 billion years ago, when the earth's outer surface had formed into a number of independent but interlocking 'tectonic plates'.

Tectonic plates are not stationary, but are driven around the globe by convection currents which transfer heat from the earth's 'core' towards its outer margins. The boundaries between the plates can be 'passive' or they can be 'active'. Passive plate boundaries mean that adjacent plates move together; active plate boundaries mean that adjacent plates move independently.

On active plate boundaries, the plates can slide past each other (such as happens today along the San Andreas Fault on the western side of North America). They can also pull apart from each other (as happens for example in Iceland and the mid-Atlantic Ocean and also in the rift valley of East Africa) or they can collide (most notably today along the entire 'Ring of Fire' around the Pacific Ocean and also in the Himalayas).

Plate boundaries are where we find volcanic activity, earthquakes and (as we shall see in several of the later chapters) significant upwards, downwards and sideways movements of great chunks of the earth's 'crust' in the process known as 'mountain building'. Where the plates pull apart or collide, parts of the earth's 'mantle' and the lower parts of the plates themselves are melted and then erupted in the form of molten magma onto the earth's surface. The magma then cools and hardens into 'igneous' or 'volcanic' rock.

It is generally thought that only oceanic plates were created in the very early part of the earth's history. When two such oceanic plates collided, one would be forced back down into the earth's mantle in a process known as 'subduction' (see Diagrams 1.1 and 5.1). Some of the descending oceanic plate might escape subduction however, instead being ripped away from the descending plate and becoming jammed up on the surface at the point where the two plates collided. Subduction zones also generate volcanic activity, and this too creates new rock. These combined effects led to the formation of the first continental rocks and, over time, to the development of continental plates.

There are two types of tectonic plate: 'continental plate' and 'oceanic plate'. The basic distinction is obvious, although a continental plate can extend some distance out below sea level with a 'continental shelf'. The key difference is that oceanic plates are thin and dense, while continental plates are thick and less dense. Another important difference is that oceanic

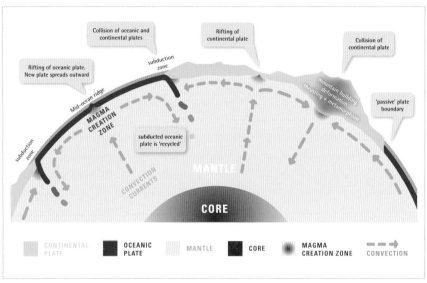

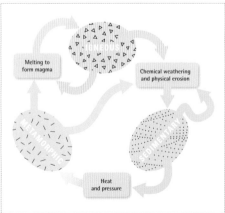

Diagram 1.1 | Structure of the earth.

Diagram 1.2 | Simplified 'rock cycle' of igneous, sedimentary and metamorphic rocks.

plates, being constantly recycled by subduction, are no older than 200 million years whereas continental plate can be up to a few billion years old.

Geologists reckon that water was present in significant quantities on the earth's surface from quite early in its history, forming both oceans and an atmosphere with weather and rain. This meant that the rocks forming the continents were subject to erosion by wind, water and ice, resulting in the eroded fragments of rock being dumped as 'sediment' into coastal waters. This material accumulated and was slowly transformed into 'sedimentary' rocks.

As the continental plates grew in size it was inevitable that they too would be driven into collision by the earth's inner convection currents. When two continental plates collided however, there was no subduction. Instead, the plates were crushed and crumpled. The rocks forming the continental plate (of both igneous and sedimentary origin) were forced up into great mountain ranges and were subject to so much heat and pressure that they were transformed internally. These are what geologists call 'metamorphic' rocks.

Over the billions of intervening years the continental plates have grown in size and have, roughly every 500 million years, been driven by the earth's inner convection currents to collect together to form a supercontinent. The supercontinents did not survive long before breaking up to wander the earth as independent continents, often colliding into one another, building mountain ranges and metamorphosing the rocks. The continental plates have also collided with oceanic plates, generating more episodes of subduction and volcanic activity.

Such events have left their distinct marks in the landscape of the Scottish Highlands, which contains a great variety of igneous, sedimentary and metamorphic rocks from a great spread of ages. The rocks of the far northwest of Scotland were formed as long as 3 billion years ago. On the other hand, the volcanic rocks of Ardnamurchan (and of Mull, Skye, Arran and some other islands) were created 'just' 60 million years ago during incredibly violent eruptions accompanying the break-up of a continental plate (into the North American and the European plates) and the creation of a new ocean. This ocean then widened to its present extent, and is known today as the Atlantic Ocean (see Chapter 10).

From our human perspective, 60 million years is no more comprehensible than 3 billion. Despite that, some simple arithmetic tells us that the rocks of the far northwest are all of 50 times older than those of Ardnamurchan. The difference can be compared to that between a 1-year-old child and a 50-year-old adult. The last 60 million years are of little significance when weighted against the history of the earth, but still remain beyond our wildest imagination.

The tectonic plates may only move a few centimetres a year, but over a few million years they can travel hundreds of kilometres. Sedimentation may add just a millimetre a year to the top of accumulating sand, silt or mud, but over a few million years that can add up to thousands of metres of solid rock. Erosion may only reduce mountains by a few millimetres in a decade, but over tens of millions of years it can wear them down to lowly stumps.

The earth's processes ceaselessly create new continental rocks, then wear them down only to rebuild them anew alongside the old rock: the earth's surface is a work in progress. Having looked at some of the theory behind plate tectonics and our understanding of the earth, it is time to turn our attention to the very oldest of Scottish rocks and seek evidence in the scenery of those processes at work back in the dim and distant past.

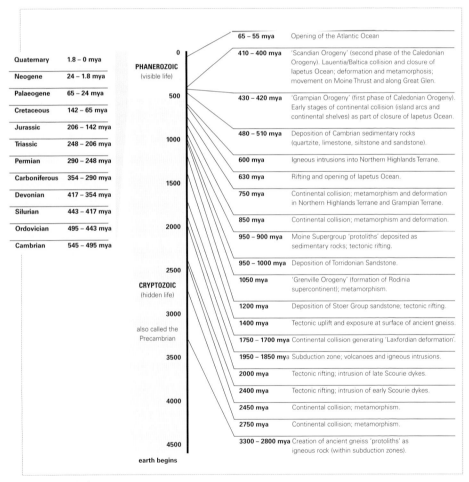

			65 – 55 mya	Opening of the Atlantic Ocean
Quaternary	1.8 – 0 mya	0	410 – 400 mya	'Scandian Orogeny' (second phase of the Caledonian Orogeny). Lauentia/Baltica collision and closure of Iapetus Ocean; deformation and metamorphosis; movement on Moine Thrust and along Great Glen.
		PHANEROZOIC (visible life)		
Neogene	24 – 1.8 mya			
Palaeogene	65 – 24 mya	500	430 – 420 mya	'Grampian Orogeny' (first phase of Caledonian Orogeny). Early stages of continental collision (island arcs and continental shelves) as part of closure of Iapetus Ocean.
Cretaceous	142 – 65 mya			
Jurassic	206 – 142 mya		480 – 510 mya	Deposition of Cambrian sedimentary rocks (quartzite, limestone, siltstone and sandstone).
		1000		
Triassic	248 – 206 mya			
Permian	290 – 248 mya		600 mya	Igneous intrusions into Northern Highlands Terrane.
Carboniferous	354 – 290 mya	1500	630 mya	Rifting and opening of Iapetus Ocean.
Devonian	417 – 354 mya		750 mya	Continental collision; metamorphism and deformation in Northern Highlands Terrane and Grampian Terrane.
Silurian	443 – 417 mya		850 mya	Continental collision; metamorphism and deformation.
Ordovician	495 – 443 mya	2000	950 – 900 mya	Moine Supergroup 'protoliths' deposited as sedimentary rocks; tectonic rifting.
Cambrian	545 – 495 mya			
		2500	950 – 1000 mya	Deposition of Torridonian Sandstone.
		CRYPTOZOIC (hidden life)	1050 mya	'Grenville Orogeny' (formation of Rodinia supercontinent); metamorphism.
		3000	1200 mya	Deposition of Stoer Group sandstone; tectonic rifting.
		also called the Precambrian	1400 mya	Tectonic uplift and exposure at surface of ancient gneiss.
			1750 – 1700 mya	Continental collision generating 'Laxfordian deformation'.
		3500	1950 – 1850 mya	Subduction zone; volcanoes and igneous intrusions.
			2000 mya	Tectonic rifting; intrusion of late Scourie dykes.
			2400 mya	Tectonic rifting; intrusion of early Scourie dykes.
		4000	2450 mya	Continental collision; metamorphism.
			2750 mya	Continental collision; metamorphism.
		4500	3300 – 2800 mya	Creation of ancient gneiss 'protoliths' as igneous rock (within subduction zones).
		earth begins		

Diagram 1.3 | Geological events in the Scottish Highlands (not to scale). mya (millions of years ago).

CHAPTER 2

Gnarly Gneiss

The story of the Scottish Highlands begins about 3 billion years ago. It was then that the earliest rocks that today make up large parts of the western seaboard of northern Scotland, both on the mainland and on several islands, were first created by volcanoes in 'subduction' zones (see Chapter 1).

These rocks are often referred to in books as the oldest in the world. Although it would be nice to confirm this assertion, sadly it is not true. Rocks over 4 billion years old have been found in Canada and slightly younger ones in Southern Africa, Australia and Siberia. However, the ancient 'gneiss' of Scotland's northwest is certainly extremely old – far, far older than any other rocks found in Britain today.

'Gneiss' is a form of 'metamorphic' rock. This means that the original rock has been internally changed through the long-term application of intense levels of heat and pressure, long after the rock was originally created. Such conditions only exist low down in the earth's crust during the collision of continental plates and in subduction zones (see Chapter 6).

Diagram 2.1 |

Ancient gneiss outcrops
in northwest Scotland.

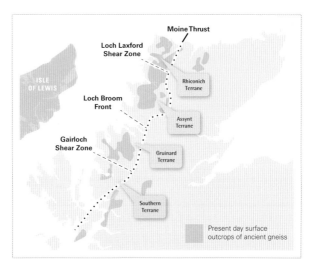

Gneiss is found on the Scottish mainland in the top north-western corner of the Highlands and further south on or close to the coast (see Diagram 2.1). Patches also outcrop further east on the mainland, but these are not major outcrops. More importantly, there are also several outcrops of gneiss on Scottish islands, notably the Isles of Harris and Lewis. The latter island, which is wholly made up of gneiss, accounts for more gneiss than all the mainland outcrops added together. As a result, geologists have named these rocks as the 'Lewisian Gneiss'. They have also given the same name to the mainland gneiss rocks. However, in order to avoid confusion, I will refer throughout this book to the 'ancient gneiss'.

To appreciate the processes that created the ancient gneiss, we need to go back to the birth of the original rocks about 3 billion years ago. The latest view is that the gneisses of northwest Scotland (including those of the Inner and Outer Hebrides) did not form at the same place. At least four distinct chunks of territory have grouped together to form the single region we recognise today. The technical term for such chunks of continent is 'terrane', and each terrane has its own geological history. They were independent entities for some 1.3 billion years, from 3 billion years ago to 1.7 billion years ago. During this long period of time they were independently created, severely bashed about by bouts of mountain building and metamorphosis, and only then conjoined.

The four terranes of northwest Scotland are, from north to south, the Rhiconich Terrane, the Assynt Terrane, the Gruinard Terrane and the Southern Region Terrane. They are divided by three 'shear zones': the Laxford Shear Zone, the Loch Broom Front and the Gairloch Shear Zone (see Diagram 2.1). The oldest is the Assynt Terrane, which was originally formed about 3 billion years ago. The other three terranes date from a little later, from about 2.8 billion years ago. However, one tiny crystal found at the southern end of the Rhiconich Terrane has been dated back to an incredible 3.35 billion years ago (near the location of Photo 2.7). The original rocks ('protoliths') of all the ancient gneisses were of igneous origin, created by volcanoes in ancient 'subduction zones' where oceanic and continental plates collided (see Chapter 1).

The first phase of metamorphosis took place at different times on the different terranes (which is essentially how geologists have worked out that they were not linked at such times). Metamorphosis occurred at about 2.7 billion years ago for the Gruinard Terrane, 2.49 billion years ago for the Assynt Terrane and 1.85 billion years ago for the Rhiconich Terrane. The first phase of metamorphosis took place in the Southern Region Terrane at some time after 2.8 billion years ago, but a more precise date is not known.

At some time, probably between 2.4 and 1.9 billion years ago, clashing tectonic plates led to a lot of magma being created at the base of the plate and then injected into the overlying rocks. The magma rose towards the surface in 'sheets' that forced their way up along 'faults', or great cracks, in the rocks. Some of the magma may have erupted onto the surface where it would have cooled to form rocks, but these rocks have now been entirely eroded away. Much of the magma however cooled down in the faults before reaching the surface, forming what geologists call 'dykes' (see below). These are common in the Assynt Terrane.

Another phase of metamorphosis occurred about 1.7 billion years ago, again caused by the collision of continental plates. Geologists think it is likely that the individual terranes were brought together at that time. Once joined, the terranes stuck firmly together and began to share a common geological history. Indeed, the terranes are now considered jointly to form a single terrane known as the Hebridean Terrane. It is one of the five terranes that later combined to form the greater chunk of continental crust that we now call Scotland (see Diagram 6.1). Three of those five terranes form the Scottish Highlands: the Hebridean Terrane; the Northern Highlands Terrane (Chapters 5 and 6); and the Grampian Terrane (Chapter 7).

Having looked at the overall geological history, we can now turn to look at the ancient gneiss. The processes of metamorphosis will be looked at in a bit more detail in Chapters 6 and 7, but essentially great heat and pressure combine to change the crystal structure of the rocks without melting it (the processes start to occur at about one-third to one-half of the rock's melting temperature). These processes occur quite deep in the earth's crust, at some 20km or more below the surface. The heat and pressure causes 'ions' within the mineral crystal grains to move from one grain to another, forming chemically different crystals (see Chapter 6). The crystals may also undergo 'plastic deformation' where they can be stretched and bent without losing their cohesion, as opposed to 'brittle deformation' where the rocks crack (see Chapter 7).

One feature that is quite common in the ancient gneiss is 'banding'. This is created during metamorphosis when different minerals present in the original rocks separate and segregate into layers of like minerals. As the crystal grains exchange ions, the great pressures force the developing crystals to migrate and seek shelter from the intense forces acting on the grain boundaries by fitting into groups of similar shapes (see Photo 2.1). Sometimes these bands or layers can also be deformed into folds (see Photos 2.2 and 2.3). Deformation and metamorphosis are often found together in rock outcrops; they are intimately linked processes often occurring at the same time (although metamorphosis also occurs without immediate evidence of deformation).

Photo 2.1 | Banded gneiss boulder, weathered face, Beinn Cannaboinc.

Photo 2.2 | Folded banded gneiss, fairly fresh face, small-scale example 7.5cm across at Beinn Eighe visitor centre.

Photo 2.3 | Folded gneiss, well-weathered face, medium-scale example 1.5m high near Tarbet.

One important point to note is that all rocks are subject to chemical weathering as soon as they are exposed to the atmosphere. This changes the colour of the rock; in general rocks weather to a greyish colour. Where a rock has been recently broken however, it presents a 'fresh face' to the atmosphere. The fresh face is likely to look very different to the weathered face. Geologists often analyse rocks visually using the fresh face. As hillwalkers, however, we usually only see weathered rocks so this is what we will focus on here. It is worth remembering that different weathering stages make for quite different-looking rocks. Freshly broken gneiss may present a distinctly 'liquorice allsorts' face to the world (see Photo 2.2).

The ancient gneiss produces a very distinctive landscape. A bleak, gnarly and weather-beaten one is it too, and appropriately so for such staggeringly old rocks. The ancient gneiss landscape of the northwest Highlands is known to geologists as 'knock and lochan' topography. Knock comes from the Gaelic 'cnoc' and means a low hill or mound. Lochan comes from the same tongue and means a small lake. The name is therefore very apt for the gneiss landscape which is indeed a mix of convoluted knobbly hillocks and innumerable little lakes (see Photos, 2.4, 2.5 and w2.2).

Photo 2.4 | Knock and lochan topography from ground level, near Scourie.

Photo 2.5 | Knock and lochan topography from above, looking west from Quinag.

Given its age, the gneiss has been thoroughly eroded over the hundreds of millions of years exposing a 'grain' in the rocks. This general grain of the land represents weathering and erosion along lines of weakness in the rocks, such as along the line of ancient faults and/or rock boundaries within the gneiss. The faults are cracks in the rocks created by tectonic activity such as compression of two plates when they collide, or by stretching of the plates when they pull apart.

This landscape grain is not readily evident on the ground, where the distribution of ups and downs seems either wholly random or even purposely designed to make progress on foot extremely hard work at best. The cover of heather-dominated vegetation is extremely rough, with innumerable concealed boulders and holes making for painful progress. The lochans often force long diversions and are sometimes surrounded by widespread patches of boggy ground that add to the challenging mix.

However, the grain is not totally hidden on the ground and occasional vistas bring it to the fore. The grain is often quite evident from higher viewpoints. Photo w2.2 illustrates this, taken from near the summit area of Ben Stack looking northwest. A general grain of major lines can be seen in the photo running across from upper left to lower right, with a particularly noticeable feature in the centre and centre right. A subsidiary grain is seen running from lower right to upper left. This represents internal rock boundaries, while the former grain represents deeper faults and tectonic structures. The visible line in the centre and centre-right of the photo, which can just about be discerned tracing off in the centre left, is part of the Laxford Shear Zone between the two northernmost gneiss terranes (as is the area immediately below the grass in the lower-left corner of the photo).

The ancient gneiss covers vast areas of northwest Scotland: areas that see very few, if any, walkers. There are however some good routes across the knock and lochan topography in places, such as the twisting track between Scourie and Tarbet. Here you are among some of the most ancient of the ancient gneisses, led through innumerable hollows and around plenty of lochans, between rough, gnarly 'knocks'. Frequently the view is limited to a hundred metres or so of the immediate area (see Photo 2.4), and tracks often bypass the knocks keeping you low down and without wider views. Yet now and again, a wider view opens out and this ancient landscape is revealed in its stark beauty (see Photo 1.4).

In this area you will also see evidence of some of the tectonic activity which occurred after the gneiss had been formed. The gneiss has been 'intruded' into by scores of igneous 'dykes'. These are vertical sheets of once molten magma that pushed its way up into the gneiss when it lay well below ground level. The molten magma cooled and solidified into rock without reaching the surface. These intrusive rocks are particularly common in this area and are known as the 'Scourie dykes'. See Photo 2.8 which show a dyke running up a gneiss outcrop near Tarbet.

Photo 2.6 | Intrusive dyke cutting through gneiss near Tarbet.

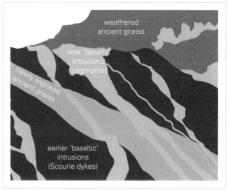

Photo 2.7 + Diagram 2.2 | Roadside cutting near Loch Laxford on the A838 (the evenly spaced lines are drilling holes for making the cutting). The basaltic 'Scourie dykes' have cut across the ancient gneiss, then granitic dykes have later cut across both earlier rock types. The oldest known rock fragment in Scotland is taken from here and is estimated to be 3.35 billion years old; most of the gneiss around here is between 3 and 2.7 billion years old.

Photo 2.7 shows two different sets of dykes cutting through ancient gneiss at a road cutting near Lochinver. This illustrates two separate episodes of the intrusion of molten magma into the gneiss. The stark colours are the result of this being a new cutting; we can see a pretty fresh face (the grey weathered face is visible at the top of the photograph). Patches of reddish rock indicate the presence of dykes in the weathered face, but the fresh face shows so much more vivid detail. The near-vertical parallel lines are marks left by drills driven into the rock to make the cutting. Contrast this recently exposed outcrop with the well-weathered rocks seen in Photo 2.6.

Well before 1.2 billion years ago, a major change occurred in this area of the earth. The metamorphosed rocks were raised from their position deep in the earth's crust, eventually even reaching the surface. This was the result of tectonic activity forcing the rocks upwards during compression of the plates as a result of continental collision. Eventually the gneiss was exposed at the surface. It was then immediately subject to erosion, a process which carved a landscape of low hills and valleys into the gneiss.

From about 1.2 billion years ago, the area was inundated by rivers. These carried down eroded fragments as sand which was dumped on top of the gneiss. This sand was then transformed into sandstone (known as the Torridonian sandstone as we will see in the next chapter). In a few places, later erosion has left us with cross-sections cut vertically through the rocks where we can see the gneiss landscape onto which the sand was dumped.

A good site for this is the Beinn Eighe northern visitor centre car park (NH 001 649) next to Loch Maree (or better still from viewpoints as described in Walk 5). The geology is fairly complex around here (see Chapter 5), but almost directly opposite on Slioch the situation is fairly straightforward and a valley can be easily seen in the gneiss with sandstone sitting on top (see Photo 2.8).

The ancient gneiss of northwest Scotland thus forms the 'basement' (or 'foreland') on which later rocks of the Highlands were deposited by volcanoes and repeated cycles of sedimentation. Although highly weathered, the landscape of the region gives the hillwalker a highly privileged view back across an amazing two-thirds of the earth's geological history.

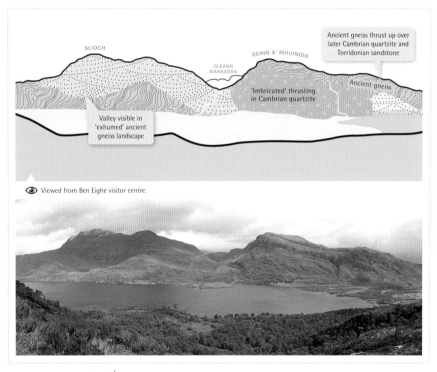

Viewed from Ben Eighe visitor centre.

Photo 2.8 + Diagram 2.3 | Valley in ancient gneiss landscape underneath overlying Torridonian sandstone.

CHAPTER 3

Torrid Torridonian

The enchanting and varied landscape of northwest Scotland is a complex mix of two main rock types. These rocks are the basement of ancient gneiss, which we looked at in the previous chapter, and great thicknesses of largely reddish sandstone. Known as the Torridonian sandstone, it sits directly on top of the gneiss and is the subject of this chapter. In Assynt, Torridon and Applecross this mix of gneiss and sandstone creates some of Scotland's most compelling scenery.

Although Cape Wrath itself is made of ancient gneiss, there are Torridonian sandstone outcrops in the immediate area of the cape and also nearby in the low hills such as Fashven and Creag Riabhach. Shielding the north-western corner of Britain from both view and easy access, these low rolling hills do not offer the most immediately exciting scenery when seen from the road. For those who trek to Cape Wrath on foot via Sandwood Bay, however, this is one of Britain's wildest landscapes.

There is little Torridonian sandstone in the area from south of Oldshoremore (near Kinlochbervie) until the Assynt area. This latter region is justly famed for its sandstone scenery, however. Although sandstone outcrops are limited in extent, they are separated by vast low areas of gneiss and the coast. These create the classic 'knock and lochan' topography discussed in the previous chapter, but with the appearance of isolated hills rising above the gneiss landscape. It is in this area that the sandstone begins to offer such spectacular scenery, richly rewarding the many landscape lovers who undertake the long journey to reach the region and enjoy its unrivalled hillwalking opportunities. The walk described on and around Quinag (see Walk 3) provides a prime example of the bleak landscape.

Assynt's isolated sandstone peaks are effectively island mountains ('inselbergs') poking out above the seething ocean of gneiss (see Photo 3.1). The long, thin, steep-sided hills such as Quinag, Canisp, Suilven and Stac Pollaidh rear up out of the bleak 'knock and lochan' topography of the ancient gneiss and typify this haunting landscape. The sandstone covered the whole area many millions of years ago, but much of it has been eroded away to leave this stunning landscape (see Diagram 3.1).

Photo 3.1 │ Sandstone scenery of Assynt: isolated sandstone hills rise up from 'knock and lochan' topography in ancient gneiss. Left to right: Ben More Coigach, Cul Beag, Cul Mor, Suilven and Canisp.

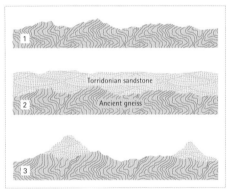

Diagram 3.1 │ (1) Ancient gneiss is exposed at the surface and eroded in undulating landscape by about 1.2 billion years ago; (2) Torridonian sandstone laid down when ancient gneiss is flooded by large rivers between 1.2 and 0.8 billion years ago; and (3) Torridonian sandstone has now been eroded into isolated mountains in northwest Scotland.

The sandstone becomes much more extensive south of the Assynt area, covering the whole of the north-western 'terrane' (see Chapter 2) between the Moine Thrust Zone to the east and the coast to the west. The mountains become broader and form massifs (see Photo 3.2). South of Loch Broom the basement area is wider and the sandstone remains extensive, but the ancient gneiss outcrops on the earth's surface in a few places. The situation changes again roughly south of Loch Maree where the gneiss again thins out to be replaced entirely by the overlying sandstone. By the time we reach the Applecross peninsula, the ancient gneiss is found only to the east of the great Moine Thrust Zone, where it has either been displaced by massive earth movements (see Chapter 5) or is an exposed part of the underlying basement.

These areas of more extensive Torridonian sandstone outcrops produce some of the Highlands' most magnificent mountains: An Teallach (between Little Loch Broom and Loch

Photo 3.2 | Sandstone mountain, Bheinn Bhan, Applecross.

Photo 3.3 | An Teallach, a mountain of sandstone and possibly the finest mountain view in mainland Britain.

Maree); the clump of immensely popular mountains, Ben Alligin, Liathach and Beinn Eighe (between Loch Maree and Loch Torridon); and Beinn Bhan (on Applecross peninsula). These are not the narrow islands seen in Assynt, but significantly more substantial structures.

Strathnasheallag Forest, Fisherfield Forest and Letterewe Forest, which form the great clump of land sitting between Loch Broom and Loch Maree, are home to some of Britain's finest mountains. Except for the peripheral areas, access is by foot (or boat) and many trips require multi-day walks. Just about accessible by a long day's walk is An Teallach; this is possibly the most impressive mountain in mainland Britain (see Photo 3.3), especially the views of and from the oddly named peak of Lord Berkeley's Seat. The pointed peak actually overhangs Coire Toll an Lochain and just looking towards it can be vertigo-inducing. The full ridge traverse is a stunning but exposed scramble. Less frightening outings can be had by approaching the ridge from either end and turning back when you've reached the limits of your tolerance. An Teallach, like all the other Torridonian sandstone hills, has a distinctive shape marked by a very definite horizontal lineation known as 'bedding' or 'strata'. These beds represent the episodes of creation of the sandstone rock from loose grains of 'sand' dumped in ancient rivers, lakes and shallow seas.

Sand may be a pretty familiar thing, but for geologists it has a very specific definition. Any rock fragment that is between 0.0625 and 2mm in size is a sand grain. It matters not what the content of the rock fragment is. Only its size matters. Fragments smaller than 0.0625mm are called 'silt' and smaller still are known as 'mud'. Fragments bigger than 2mm are called 'gravel' and bigger still are known as 'pebbles'. The name doesn't tell you anything about the content of the mud particle, the sand grain or the pebble.

Photo 3.4 | A close-up of Torridonian sandstone, showing individual sand grains cemented into solid rock.

However, there is some correspondence between size and content. It is estimated that about 70% of sand grains in the world are made of quartz (also known as silica). This is a physically very hard and fairly chemically inert mineral. Sand can also be formed from other minerals, but then is usually only a transitional stage before becoming smaller (and eventually becoming silt or mud particles).

Clay minerals are much more vulnerable to physical and chemical erosion and become much smaller than the size needed to qualify as sand, so they produce silt and mud (and eventually become siltstone and mudstone). Being highly resistant, quartz fragments are much more likely to be found in the size which fits the definition of sand. The Torridonian sandstone falls into this category and consists of small grains of quartz. It also contain large grains forming gravel and pebbles, but not in sufficient proportion to affect the general classification of the rock as 'sandstone'.

On present-day earth, it is estimated that about 8 billion cubic metres of material is eroded every year from the continents and dumped at sea as sediment in the form of grains of mud and sand. In a mountainous area such as the Himalayas, about 30cm depth of material is removed every 1,000 years to be carried away and dumped in rivers and seas.

These same processes of erosion and deposition of sediments in seas and rivers were happening 1.2 billion to 800 million years ago. As we saw in the previous chapter, for several millions of years the mountains of the ancient gneiss basement had been exposed at the surface and were eroded into a landscape of ups and downs. Around 1.2 billion years ago, the land began to subside due to the stretching of the continental plate in this area as it was pulled apart by the earth's internal convection currents.

The stretching would have been accommodated by movement along great faults (cracks in the crust or outer part of the continental plate). Large areas of land would have dropped down along the lines of these faults, moving only a few centimetres (or occasionally a few metres) at a time but repeatedly over many millions of years. The result would have been the formation of large 'basins' bounded by the faults.

Large rivers then carried material (eroded from gneiss mountains in the northwest) down towards the subsiding basins, there dumping the sedimentary material. The sand would have fallen out of suspension in shifting river channels in floodplains and lowland areas and also in lakes and in shallow seas. Countless quantities of material was eroded, transported and dumped. So much weight of material was dumped as sediments that it began to depress the solid mantle rocks beneath the tectonic plate, deepening the already subsiding basin. As a result, great thicknesses of sediment accumulated in the rivers, lakes and shallow seas without them becoming entirely choked with sand and finer material.

The dumping of trillions and trillions of sand grains continued for some 400 million years overall. Up to 5,000m of 'sandstone' were created as a result in the central area of the outcrop. It was less thick to the north, although still reaching as much as 2,000m thick in places.

The process by which loose 'sand' becomes transformed into 'sandstone' is known as 'diagenesis'. As more sand grains were deposited, the combined weight of all the sediments grew and grew. Upper layers pressed down on lower layers, squeezing out most water (except from tiny pores in the sand). Some grains even dissolved under the pressure, while other minerals precipitated out of the remaining water. These chemical changes cemented the loose grains together to form a solid rock.

Some time after 800 million years ago, the long, slow process of the accumulation of rock from dumped sand drew to a close. Sea level fell and the Torridonian rocks were exposed for a few million years before sea level once again engulfed the area and more rocks were laid down on top of the sandstone (see Chapter 4).

Later, all these rocks were again pushed upwards above sea level by the collision of continental plates. Overlying rocks have since then been largely eroded away, exposing the sandstone or removing it altogether in places (exposing its ancient gneiss basement). Considerable quantities of material have been removed; today we see only the last remnants of the great sandstone mountains that once graced this region.

Since the sandstone was first created, the Highlands area has undergone considerable tectonic activity and extremely violent volcanoes have burst through to the surface. The collision of continental plates resulted in nearby mountain building which led to intense tilting, the deformation of rocks and metamorphosis. The Torridonian sandstone remained almost untouched however, displaying only a slight tilt in contrast to the intense folding of rocks to the south and east. The Torridonian sandstone also evaded metamorphosis, and only a very few igneous intrusions have been injected into the mass of sandstone. The reason for this seems to be that the very hard gneiss basement has been strong enough to resist tectonic compression during recent episodes of mountain building (490–390 million years ago), by and large protecting the overlying sandstones. Only in the great Moine Thrust Zone (see Chapter 5) has the sandstone been seriously disrupted in a few places.

Overall, this means that despite its considerable age, the sandstone retains many of its original features both in the distant view of the layered beds and in the close detail of the rock.

The individual grains of sand that collected into sandstone are often visible in the outcrops or broken lumps (see Photo 3.4). In many places, the individual sediments are large enough to be classified as gravel or pebbles. Some of these lumps are quite substantial but have been cemented into the rock just like the smaller sand grains (see Photo 3.10). It is often possible to see the 'grading' of beds where larger fragments and pebbles dominate in the lower part of a bed. The faster the current, the larger the particles that can be carried by moving water. Heavier particles drop out of the flow sooner than lighter grains and accumulate at the base of 'beds', producing 'graded bedding' (see Photo 3.10).

The Torridonian sandstones display clear 'bedding', the term used to describe the more or less horizontal lines that demarcate different layers within the rock. Each layer represents a continuous period of sedimentation and each bedding line between the layers represents some sort of break or change in the process. Bedding lines often form points of weaknesses where erosion can get to work once the rock is exposed to the atmosphere. Indeed, erosion picks out and emphasises these lines, giving the Torridonian sandstone hills their characteristic layered look (see Photos 3.5 and 3.6).

Geologists believe that the Torridonian sandstones were mainly laid down in broad, braided rivers where the river channels would frequently have shifted course. In doing so, the shifting channel would cut across previous bedding lines, laying new beds on top. As these bedding lines represent ripple structures on the floor of the river they are not horizontal, so a new stream course slices through older ripples. This creates a feature known as 'cross-bedding' and is very common in the Torridonian sandstone (and other sedimentary rocks, to be seen in later chapters). Cross-bedding is illustrated in Photos 3.7 and 3.8, and the ripples which can sometimes be exposed on the surface of a bedding plane are depicted in Photo 3.9.

Another frequent feature of the Torridonian sandstone is the presence of 'jointing'. These cracks are created when the sandstone contracts slightly as it dries out during the transformation from loose sand to solid sandstone, which occurs shortly after being laid down. Once exposed on the surface by erosion of overlying rocks, the joints offer an increased area of exposed surface; this allows increased chemical weathering to bite deep into a rock. Water can also

Photo 3.5 | Horizontal bedding on Spidean Cóinich seen from Sáil Gharbh, Quinag.

Photo 3.6 | Beinn na h-Eaglaise seen from Maol Chean Dearg.

Photos 3.7 + 3.8 | Cross-bedding seen in Torridonian sandstone.

Photo 3.9 | Ripples
on a lump of Torridonian
sandstone; sample
is 20cm long.

Photo 3.10 | Graded bedding in Torridonian sandstone near Ardmair: a clear bedding line
marked out by pebbles which have fallen to the base of the bed, with largely gravel above.

get into the joints and freeze, expanding slightly, then thawing. Further cycles of freeze-thaw
action can start to break open the rock outcrops into boulders and pebbles (see Photo w7.2).

Joints are often confused with scratches made by glaciers dragging rock fragments over
the bedrock, but they are quite different features. An example of glacial scratches or striations
is shown in Photo w16.7. Such marks are pretty much straight, parallel and not very deep at
all, whereas the sandstone jointing is irregular, often curving and deeper (although jointing
can take regular form in some igneous rocks, as seen on Walk 16 in Glen Coe).

Today we meet sand on beaches or alongside rivers and lakes, but loose sand can also be found in mountain areas. Indeed, you will come across sandy patches on all the recommended walks in this book that traverse any of the outcrops of Torridonian sandstone, derived from the sandstone rock outcrops.

When the sandstone is exposed to the surface it immediately begins to undergo chemical weathering. This breaks down the material which cements together the individual sand grains in the sandstone. The sand grains are released and collect on the ground to form sandy patches. When the wind is strong, it whips up the sand grains and uses them as very effective agents of physical erosion – literally sandblasting the rock.

One other feature of some of the Torridonian rocks deserves a mention, although not visible to the hillwalker. Geologists have recently been looking very closely at some 'microfossils' dating from as far back as 1 billion years ago, common around the Loch Torridon area. Previously they were thought to be very basic life forms, but geologists now realise that they are in fact fairly complex. This has presented a further challenge to accepted ideas which believed that complex life was not to be found outside of the oceans in these ancient times, only appearing much later. Until these discoveries, no previous examples of such 'eukaryote' life forms had been found from 'land' (albeit within ancient lake deposits) as opposed to within the seas.

The Torridonian rocks have clearly not yet revealed all they can tell us about the world in which they were created. The various features we have looked at, however, combine to make a very distinctive landscape, with the layering of the bedding the most conspicuous medium-range factor. The layering is often best seen in the great glacial 'corries' (see Chapter 11) which litter the hills. It was in these corries that glaciers cut down into the rock, eroding more effectively along the lines of bedding and jointing and giving the mountains their shape (see Photos 11.9, w7.1 and w7.5).

As mentioned above, the Torridonian hills of Assynt are today separate entities ('island mountains' or 'inselbergs') sticking up out of the gneiss basement. At one time however, these isolated peaks of reddish sandstone were joined in a continuous covering of sandstone which was laid down across the entire area of the ancient gneiss.

More rocks were later laid down on top of the sandstone, in particular a sandstone forming a rock called 'sedimentary quartzite'. Several Torridonian hills have survived until today because they are topped with a smallish layer of quartzite which provides a resistant capping. Stac Pollaidh is an example of a hill which has now lost its quartzite cap; it is rather like the rotted stump of a tooth barely poking up above the surrounding scree and vegetation (see Photo 3.11).

Photo 3.11 | Stac Pollaidh: the last fragments of an 'inselberg'
or 'island' mountain being eroded away.

In a short geological time (but still a very hefty one in human terms) all of the much-loved Torridonian sandstone mountains will be reduced to Stac Pollaidh-like stumps. On a somewhat longer timescale, the Torridonian sandstone will be entirely eroded away exposing more of the underlying gneiss. The gneiss will then be further eroded until tectonic activity or some other factor causes a rise in relative sea levels. More new material will then be dumped on top of the remaining sandstone or volcanoes will spew out more new rocks in the age-long rock cycles driven by plate tectonics.

CHAPTER 4

Cambrian Capping

It would be handy in this story, as we progress through time and space in the Scottish Highlands, if we could simply move as in previous chapters from the older to younger rocks, following the upwards accumulation of more recent rocks on top of earlier rocks. In the previous chapter we saw how the Torridonian sandstone lies directly on top of the ancient gneiss, albeit with a long period of time between them.

Logically, this chapter ought to deal with the rocks that followed the Torridonian sandstone in time. These would be the rocks known to geologists as the 'Moine', which mainly occur a bit further over to the east and will be covered in Chapter 6. Instead, in this chapter, we will jump ahead and look first at some rocks that only came into existence after the Moine rocks had been created. This is not an attempt to be awkward. The choice is actually determined by the geology and it makes sense to continue our scenic journey through the Highlands with the rocks that come next spatially, if not temporally.

The rocks which sit on top of the Torridonian sandstone and, in some places, directly on top of ancient gneiss, originated in the time that geologists call the Cambrian period. It lasted from 545 to 495 million years ago (see Diagram 1.3 for a depiction of the geological periods). These rocks today outcrop as a pretty slender strip, usually narrower than 5km wide, that runs all the way down from Loch Eriboll on the northern coast to the head of Loch Kishorn at the south-eastern corner of the Applecross peninsula. Although quite narrow, the north–south extent of the outcrop is about 150km (see Diagram 5.2).

In a few places (around Durness, in the Assynt area and south of Kinlochewe) the Cambrian rocks are not confined to quite such a lanky strip and are slightly more extensive. In Assynt, the Cambrian outcrops measure some 20km across.

Although generally narrow in extent, the outcrop of the Cambrian rocks is of major geological and scenic importance. Hills such as Foinaven and Arkle (Walk 1) in the north, Breabag (Walk 4) in Assynt and An Ruadh Stac near Lochcarron (see Photo 4.1) are all exceptionally attractive and all mainly formed from Cambrian rocks.

Photo 4.1 | An Ruadh Stac, formed of Cambrian quartzite and tilted to nearly 45° degrees (lower right to upper left).

Photo 4.2 | The summit ridge of Liathach formed mainly of Torridonian sandstone, but with a pointed capping of light-coloured Cambrian quartzite visible on the summit point, centre left, Spidean a' Choire Leith.

Perhaps even more important in scenic terms is the role of the Cambrian rocks in helping to define the shape of some of the mountains formed by the Torridonian sandstone and which we looked at in the previous chapter. Tough Cambrian rocks cap several of the isolated peaks of Assynt: Quinag, Canisp and Cul Mor among them. Further south, Cambrian rocks also top such fine peaks as Mullach Coire Mhic Fhearchair, Beinn Eighe and Liathach (see Photo 4.2).

Without the tough capping of Cambrian rocks, many of these hills would be less resistant to erosion. Stac Pollaidh illustrates what happens when one of the isolated Assynt hills loses its resistant Cambrian cap. Today it resembles a rotted stump (see Photo 3.11). Other Torridonian sandstone hills that lack a Cambrian cap have been eroded into low, layered hills (see Photo 3.6).

The Cambrian rocks are all of sedimentary origin, having been laid down in shallow seas that inundated the entire area covering the earlier ancient gneiss and Torridonian sandstone. They include some fascinating outcrops of a type of rock known as 'limestone' (see box 'Cambrian limestone'), and there are some siltstones and sandstones that also outcrop today. However, the main part of the Cambrian outcrops is a formed of a rock known as 'quartzite'.

This is unfortunately a source of confusion, as the name 'quartzite' is usually given to rocks which were originally formed as sandstones but which have been affected by metamorphosis (where heat and pressure have changed the internal structure of the sand grains; see Chapter 7). Metamorphic quartzite contains over 80% quartz (or silica). Metamorphic quartzite is quite common in the Scottish Highlands and is found, for example, in the Mamores and Grey Corries.

The Cambrian quartzite we are dealing with in this chapter has not been subject to metamorphism and, although called quartzite, is of direct sedimentary origin (sometimes known as 'quartzose sandstone'). It is said to be a very 'mature' sedimentary rock, which means that it has been bashed around a lot by waves. This 'mechanical abrasion' has reduced any particles formed of minerals other than quartz to a tiny size. Currents have then washed away the tiny particles, leaving a near-pure collection of sand-grain-sized quartz particles which were eventually transformed into rock with a very high proportion of quartz (up to 99%). The sand grains in this type of quartzite may well have been through several cycles of sediment–rock–sediment–rock.

The present-day Cambrian quartzite retains many of its original sedimentary features such as bedding, cross-bedding, ripples and even fossils (all features destroyed by metamorphosis). Photo 4.3 shows cross-bedding in quartzite, while Photo 4.4 shows ripples left by water currents on the sandy beds before they were hardened into rock. These same sedimentary features were also seen in Chapter 3 in the Torridonian sandstone. Although the Torridonian sandstone and the Cambrian quartzite both share sedimentary origins, display similar sedimentary features and are both sandstones, they are very different-looking rocks with quite different characteristics and produce very different scenery. This illustrates how variable geological features can be. Much clearly depends on the origin of the sand particles and the nature of the environment in which they were deposited as sediment.

Photo 4.3 | Cross-bedding in Cambrian quartzite, Assynt area.

Photo 4.4 | Ripples in Cambrian quartzite, Breabag, Assynt.

The Cambrian quartzite is hard, sharp and angular. It can be slippery when wet and is wearing to walk on, especially where broken and tilted at awkward angles. It also forms extensive areas of 'quartzite pavement': bare rock exposed at the surface, often where the outcrop is gently tilted and forms the slope of a hill (see Photo 4.5). Impressive quartzite pavements and bare outcrops can be seen on Walks 1, 3, 4 and 5. This is a product of the chemically resistant nature of quartz, which means that it does not break down easily to provide nutrients for the development of vegetation and soil.

Photo 4.5 | Cambrian quartzite 'pavement' with visible jointing lines crossing at right angles; Loch Maree and Slioch (centre right).

Geologists have found various fossils in these rocks including trilobites and brachiopods, although the casual walker is unlikely to spot any such specimens. Two very common fossils are fairly easy to see, however. One frequent feature of the Cambrian quartzite is a very distinct set of strata known to geologists as the 'pipe rock'. The name derives from the innumerable small pipes which can be seen in many places all the way from the north to the south in the Cambrian rock outcrops.

The pipes are thought to be worm casts emplaced in the original sandy beach. The quartzite beds containing the remains of these pipes are encountered quite frequently when walking in areas of Cambrian rocks (see Walks 1, 3, 4 and 5) and can be viewed in two forms: plan or section.

In plan they appear as small white or light-coloured circular patches in the rock, each patch having a diameter slightly less than a pencil. Often the small, rounded patches stand slightly proud of the surrounding rock (see Photo 4.6). Alternatively, the section view usually shows a set of small white or light-coloured lines in the rock, again almost as thick as a pencil though usually only as long as a pencil stub. The rock is often a pinkish colour, sometimes a fairly dark pink. At one point in Walk 4 there are two blocks of pipe rock used as steps on a track on either side of a little gully; one block is in section and the other is in plan (see Photos w4.7 and w4.8).

Another fossil to be seen in the same quartzites, but less commonly, is known as 'trumpet rock'. Some geologists think that this type of fossil is produced by the same worms as produced the pipes, but this is not certain. The trumpets are much wider than the flared trumpet-like tops of the pipes at the surface of the sandy beach filtering out food (see Photo 4.7).

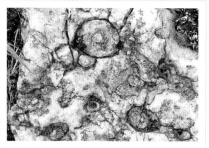

Photo 4.6 │ 'Pipe rock' is the name given to quartzite with numbers of visible worm casts (width of view 7cm).

Photo 4.7 │ Trumpet rock seen from above; width of view 10cm.

We saw earlier that the quartzite is important in the ability of Torridonian sandstone hills to resist erosion, providing a tough capping. It is the 'icing on the cake' of Beinn Eighe and several other fine Torridonian hills. The white caps of these mountains are often taken to be snow, rather than as a near-white rock.

Some of these hills (such as An Ruadh Stac) are clearly tilted at quite pronounced angles. This is the result of the collision of continental tectonic plates forcing the rocks upwards during thrusting (see Chapter 5). Others, such as Foinaven and Arkle, display only a fairly gentle tilt (see Walks 1 and 2) and on Breabag (Walk 4) you may be hard pressed to find any great tilt at all.

The rocks have actually been badly broken up and piled up into a series of tilted stacks. Again, this is the result of continental collision. As the two plates have pressed in on one another, they have crumpled and folded the rocks. In some places, this has resulted in the strata being broken up and piled into heaps or pushed ('thrust') over the top of other (perhaps younger) rocks (see Chapter 5).

This indeed is what happened within the area of the Cambrian rocks we've been looking at. At the start of this chapter I explained that we would be jumping out of the time sequence, moving from the Torridonian to the Cambrian rocks and missing out the intermediate Moine rocks. In the next chapter, we will see that the older Moine rocks often sit on top of the younger Cambrian rocks; this is why we've had to jump forward in time to the younger rocks in this chapter. The consequences of this for the scenery of the Cambrian rocks means that we will return to the area in the next chapter.

Cambrian limestone

Near Durness and especially in Assynt, but also in limited extent near Ullapool and Lochcarron, there are outcrops of some Cambrian sedimentary rocks of a type known as 'limestone'.

Limestone is a rock formed mainly from life forms such as the shells and skeletons of dead sea creatures, often in the form of calcium carbonate mud secreted by micro-organisms which devour bones and shells. It is laid down in shallow tropical seas.

Limestone is unusual in that it is a very tough rock and highly resistant to physical erosion, resulting in impressive near-vertical crags. Limestone is however easily dissolved in slightly acidic water, such as rainwater and water that has been in contact with acidic soil. This means that, over time, surface water opens up underground channels through the limestone. Water starts to drain into the rock, rather than running across it as streams and rivers as on most rocks.

The result is a bewildering array of unusual landscape features: sinkholes, powerful springs, dry valleys, caves and calcium carbonate deposits. Walk 4 through the 'Caves valley' or a walk along Traligill valley both present you with a variety of limestone features and scenery.

To appreciate quite how much limestone features vary with the amount of rainfall, it is well worth making more than one visit to these valleys if you can pick dry and wet days. In dry weather, the pretty burn draining out of the Caves valley disappears about 1km from the main road. The river bed further upstream is obviously a river bed, but is usually devoid of water (see Photo w4.2). The stream is fed instead by a spring

Photo 4.8 | Smoo Cave with water entering from a sinkhole.

Photo 4.9 | Sinkhole seen from above ground, Smoo Cave.

at the base of limestone crags on the left of the valley as you head up-valley (see Photo w4.1). The spring is not particularly conspicuous; if not keeping an eye out, it may easily be overlooked as just a muddy patch in the path.

In wet weather, however, the river bed is not dry beyond the first spring. Instead, it sports a stream which is supplied from another spring a couple of hundred metres further on (see Photos w4.4 and w4.5). This spring lies away from the valley side and looks deceptively calm. In fact, when spouting water, the spring pours out a strong and constant flow. Higher up the valley, it is possible to find where the river disappears into the limestone.

In the nearby Traligill valley it is possible to see how nature has contrived to use two quite different features, utilising a 'thrust plane' (see Chapter 5) as a channel for water to seep into limestone (see Photo 5.5).

The underground drainage channels of the limestone are easily visible on the northern coast at Smoo Cave (just east of Durness). It is possible to tour the caves when the weather is dry, but in wet weather too much water pours through the caverns and you can only get to just within the cave entrance (see Photo 4.8). There is also a fine example of a 'sinkhole' (or 'swallow hole') above the cave where drainage water ceases to run on the surface and is diverted into underground limestone channels. This is easily seen from the footpaths giving access to the cave (see Photo 4.9).

CHAPTER 5

Thrusting Times

The old proverb states that if the mountain won't come to Mohammed, then Mohammed must to the mountain go. The meaning of the saying lies in the obvious fact that mountains are so enormous and so solid that to imagine them traversing the earth is patently foolish. In fact, this is not such a silly idea after all. Indeed, with the exception of the western seaboard, all of the Highlands north of the Great Glen have been shoved or 'thrust' tens of kilometres to the northwest. In parts of north-western Scotland along the edge of the great thrust 'sheets', we can find plenty of evidence that mountains can actually move.

This evidence can be seen most spectacularly in and around the Cambrian rocks that we looked at in the previous chapter, mainly limestone and quartzite. This area was at the front of the advancing thrust sheet and has been crumpled up rather like layers of snow in front of a snow plough, although in reality it was more of a 'rock plough' propelled by the gargantuan forces of continental collision.

A brief mention was made at the end of the previous chapter about some of the odd effects of thrusting on these Cambrian rocks and also on the ancient gneiss and Torridonian sandstone. It was noted that there were places where the Cambrian limestone had been piled up, and also that older Moine Supergroup rocks (as geologists call the rocks of the area) had been thrust on top of the younger Cambrian rocks.

In some places, particularly in Assynt and also between Loch Maree and Lochcarron, the ancient gneiss and Torridonian sandstone have also been thrust into the picture and they too can be found in odd juxtapositions. Two adjacent peaks, Meall a' Ghuibhuis (Walk 5) and Ruadh stac Beag, provide a good example. The latter has a base of older sandstone and a topping of younger quartzite, but the former is the other way around with a base of younger quartzite and a topping of older sandstone. Other examples of such odd relationships will be encountered in this chapter.

The explanation for all this confusion in rock relationships is the rough-and-tumble processes of mountain building ('orogeny' in geological jargon). When two continental plates collide there is no subduction as the two plates are of similar density. Instead, there is 'crustal shortening' and 'crustal thickening'. In other words, the plates are squeezed and respond by getting thicker, extending downwards by depressing the underlying mantle rocks and upwards by building mountain ranges. The rocks are cracked, crumpled and cooked by various processes; 'metamorphosis', 'deformation', 'thrusting', 'folding' and 'faulting' are all involved at different times and/or places within the mountain-building zone as well as igneous activity. In this chapter we will look at thrusting in particular, before turning our attention to metamorphic rocks in the following two chapters. Deformation of the rocks in different ways plays a role in all these processes.

The story starts just short of 500 million years ago with an ocean, known to geologists as the Iapetus Ocean, which was being squeezed out of existence between converging chunks of continent. Laurentia, the home of Scotland's ancient rocks (and those of northern Ireland), was moving towards Baltica and Avalonia, the latter being the home of southern Britain's rocks (and those of southern Ireland). As the two continents drew closer, the ocean plate between them was progressively destroyed by subduction. When it had been fully subducted, the two continents themselves started to clash. The collision initially involved thin continental shelves and 'island arcs' (which had been created by volcanoes in the subduction zones). In a later phase, the continents proper collided in a complex scissor-like movement with Laurentia being squeezed between Baltica and Avalonia from different sides.

The crust between the colliding continents was compressed and thickened as the rock strata were pushed both downwards and upwards. The crust was squeezed down to one-fifth of its original width during the whole mountain-building episode, with corresponding up and down expansion. This is known as the 'Caledonian Orogeny', which occurred between 490 and 390 million years ago and created the Caledonian mountain range. Remnants of the Caledonian mountains are today found in the Scottish Highlands, the Welsh mountains of Snowdonia, the English fells of the Lake District, the Irish mountains, Scandinavia and Greenland.

The whole process was highly complex, and the many different aspects will be discussed in Chapters 5-9. The way the rocks react to the great pressures and high temperatures involved in the 'crustal thickening' depends on the depth of the rocks during different phases of the great collision of plates. Rocks on the surface and at depths to a few kilometres respond to the compressive forces by cracking or faulting, suffering 'brittle deformation'. We can see these effects today in the landscape of growing mountain chains such as the Himalayas; the uppermost chunks of the continental crust are therefore riven with fault zones.

Very deep down in the crust (below 20km), the temperature is much higher and the pressures are many times greater. At these depths the rocks do not crack or fault, but undergo 'plastic' or 'ductile' deformation. When rocks are above about one-third of their melting temperature; the rocks do not melt, but the crystal grains within the rock deform without breaking (see Chapter 7). This zone is also where metamorphosis is most active (see Chapter 6).

At depths of around 10–15km however, there is an intermediate zone where the temperature is high enough for some plastic deformation to take place but also cool enough for brittle deformation to occur. The result is that weaker layers of rock suffer cracking at some point and are then thrust forwards over and on top of other stronger rocks (see Diagram 5.1). The thrusting zone occurs towards the tip of the colliding plates. Thrusts are associated with great folds in the rock known as 'nappes'. It is estimated that the Moine Thrust moved a great fold of Moine rocks between 70 and 100km to the northwest from their original home.

This all occurred well below the earth's surface. In the intervening millions of years, tectonic

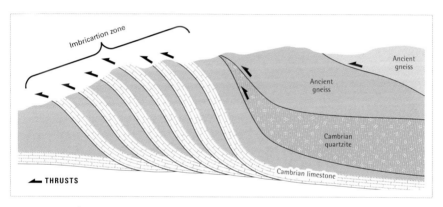

Diagram 5.1 | Moine Thrust Zone, with imbricated thrusts to the west (left) and sheet thrusts to the east (right).

forces have pushed some of the deep chunks of crust upwards. Erosion of overlying rocks have then brought the once deeply buried thrusting zone to the earth's surface for us to see in the northwest of Scotland, which geologists refer to as the 'Moine Thrust Zone'. This geologically fascinating area gives us the opportunity to peer into the middle of rock that was 10–15km into the earth's crust some 400 million years ago and see what was going on down there.

The mountain range built by the continental collision was maybe as high as the Himalayas. The folds and thrusts that have pushed chunks of the African plate on top of the European plate can be seen today in parts of the Alps (see Photo 11.4). The Alps show us what Scotland would have looked like at some stage.

The struggle among late Victorian-era geologists to understand the nature of thrust zones in mountain ranges was long and fierce. It is one of geology's founding fables, inscribing forever on sacred metaphoric rock the names of the valiant Ben Peach and John Thorne. For suggesting that older rocks could be thrust up on top of younger rocks, they earned the contempt of leading geologists who dismissed their field mapping and analysis in favour of accepted theory.

The theory of plate tectonics went through a similar struggle in the 20th century, colliding head-on with accepted theory which treated ideas of 'continental drift' as nonsense. How, it was asked, could the great masses of the continents possibly be moved for hundreds of kilometres around the surface of the earth?

Both sets of ideas are pretty much entirely accepted by geologists today. Indeed, it is through the theory of plate tectonics that the forces that thrust great masses of rocks over considerable distances are sensibly explained. The same forces that can drive the continents around the globe can also push rocks up into mountains and cause them to drop down into the depths of the crust.

The whole of the Northern Highlands Terrane (between the Moine Thrust Zone and the Great Glen) is a set of great thrust sheets that once formed the lower limbs of great nappes (see Diagram 5.1). All the upper rocks have been eroded away in the millions of years between then and now. From east to west (and thus also older to younger) there are the Swordly Thrust, the Naver Thrust, the Sgurr Beag Thrust, the Ben Hope Thrust and the Moine Thrust. The first three were probably initiated in a mountain building episode around 820–725 million years ago, and re-activated during the Caledonian Orogeny episode which created the Ben Hope and Moine thrusts.

When geologists talk about the Moine Thrust they usually mean the western limit of the great thrust sheet that brought the Moine rocks over from the southeast to sit on top of the rocks of the northwest. The underlying thrust actually extends a long way to the southeast (exactly how far is unknown) at the base of the sheet of thrust rocks, beyond our scrutiny.

We will look at the Moine rocks and the older thrusts that affected that area in Chapter 6. Here we will concentrate on a fairly narrow strip to the immediate west of the Moine Thrust, given the name of the 'Moine Thrust Zone'. This is the area I described earlier in this chapter as being like the crumpled layers of snow in front of a snow plough. Here the forces of continental collision have created a great pile-up of small-scale thrusts at the advancing front of the larger, more coherent thrust sheets such as the Moine Thrust itself. Folding and piling up of strata can be seen in the Cambrian quartzite and limestone within the Moine Thrust Zone, and thrusting is also responsible for the intriguing feature of adjacent mountains with topsy-turvy layering.

The Moine Thrust Zone runs from just east of Whiten Head on the a' Mhoine peninsula on the northern coast of Scotland, all the way to Loch Alsh on the western coast and then across the south-eastern end of Skye: a distance of some 200km. Despite its great length, the zone is quite narrow in the main (mostly less than 5km wide). It widens to as much as 15–20km in Assynt and south of Loch Maree, but in between these bulges the zone is all but negligible (see Diagram 5.2). It is the bulges which offer the most interesting geological scenery with the classic mountain landscape of Assynt and parts of Torridon.

The Moine Thrust Zone contains a mix of rocks: ancient gneiss, Torridonian sandstone and Cambrian limestone and quartzite. It is also home to a variety of thrust features. There

Diagram 5.2

Moine Thrust Zone.

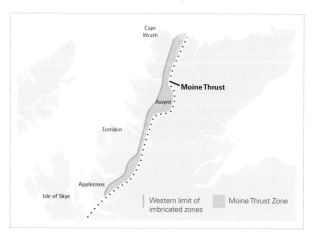

are some other medium-sized thrust sheets such as the Glencoul Thrust and the Ben More Thrust which, like the Moine Thrust but on a smaller scale, dragged a sheet of rocks some distance over the top of other rocks.

There are also areas where the thrusting has had a somewhat different effect, breaking up the rock strata and piling them up. The technical term for this is 'imbrication'. Imbrication is the arrangement of 'planar bodies' such that they stack in a consistent fashion (rather like a toppled run of dominoes). The ineluctable pressures of continental collision stretch some of the weaker layers of rocks beyond the point of cohesion, leading to 'brittle deformation'. Small thrusts then pile up the rocks, pushing them up on top of one another (see Diagram 5.1). The oldest thrust plane is nearest the source of the thrust and the highest (i.e. to the right in Diagram 5.1). The older thrusts are said to 'piggy-back' on the newer thrusts which 'carry' them forwards. Imbrication also requires 'plastic deformation'. This means that some of the rock is stretched or bent without losing its coherence, so it does not crack or fault (see box 'Deformation' in Chapter 7). As can be seen in Diagram 5.1, the piled rocks display folds at the top of each imbricated thrust (see also Photo 5.1).

It is important to remember that this breaking and thrusting is all taking place several kilometres below the surface at a depth where both brittle and plastic deformation is feasible. 'Layer cake' rocks, that is, those with fairly horizontal and well-developed bedding stratification, are more susceptible to imbrication than more 'massive' rocks. This is because the stratified rocks differ in resistance and the bed boundaries also form weaknesses; both features provide planes where the rocks can break and slide. Diagram 5.3 depicts a generalised view of how continental collision forms mountain ranges and the zone of potential thrusting and imbrication.

Having looked at the basic theory behind thrusting, we can now spot some evidence for it out in the hills. We will start where we left off in the previous chapter, with the Cambrian quartzite. Here we find plenty of evidence of imbrication, both direct and indirect.

The indirect evidence is the most immediately apparent – the repeated appearance of 'pipe rock' (see Chapter 4) in the outcrops. A walk along the tilted slope running northwest up towards the summit of Arkle (Walk 1), or up to the summit area of Breabag from Caves valley (Walk 4), will take you across regularly occurring outcrops of the easily identified pipe rock. This may not seem remarkable as rock strata are often laid down in cycles, with repeated appear-

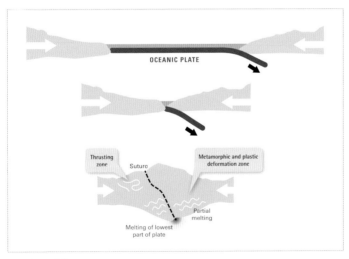

Diagram 5.3 | (1) Subduction of oceanic plate. (2) Collision of continents. (3) Mountain-building phase.

ances of a particular type of rocks. On these hills however, this feature is actually an indirect sign of imbrication. The pipe rock is not placed cyclically in the outcrop, but is in fact the base layer of the quartzite. Each outcrop of pipe rock you meet as you climb a hill is an indication that you have passed into another section of the imbricated pile of quartzite strata. To put it another way, each time you meet the pipe rock you have just passed base of a thrust.

More direct evidence of imbrication is seen in places where glaciers have carved sections through the main outcrop of quartzite. This is particularly evident on Arkle and Foinaven where the deep glacial corries and steep-sided ridges provide graphic sections through imbricated rock strata (see Photos 5.1 and w1.5).

There are also some very fine sites in Assynt such as Breabag. You can easily distinguish the quartzite thrust layers on Breabag while walking down from its summit, looking towards its northern extent (Walk 4). Here the thrusted strata look almost like petrified waves where erosion has cut clearly across each thrust line with a small rock step (see Photo w4.10).

More evidence is found in the odd rock relationships, with older rocks sitting on top of younger rocks. One of the most renowned geological sites in Scotland is a large roadside parking place on the A894 just south of Unapool, overlooking Loch Glencoul. The view here will be familiar to anyone who has looked at a geology book on the Highlands. The large lay-by offers a superb viewpoint over the Glencoul Thrust, another of the named thrusts. The base rock on the hill on the far side of the loch is ancient gneiss with Cambrian quartzite lying on top (see Photo 5.1). The quartzite itself is topped by more ancient gneiss which has been thrust from the southeast to lie on top of the younger rock. This is one of several smaller thrusts within the Moine Thrust Zone which are particularly well displayed in the Assynt region, where the zone bulges into a wide area.

The view from the parking place has been described as 'quite the best view of a thrust fault anywhere in the British Isles'. Its prominence is in fact partly due to its roadside location,

Photo 5.1 | Folded, imbricated thrusting in Cambrian quartzite, Arkle.

giving geologists and tourists alike an effortless overview of a spectacular geological feature. For the hillwalker however, there are bigger, broader and better views to be had within the Assynt area by walking up the local hills. The higher views show the Glencoul Thrust as a lengthy linear feature crossing the mountainsides and not just as a loch-side feature (as you might think seeing it only from the roadside viewing point). One such place is atop the shapely peak of Quinag (see Walk 3); from the summit ridge in particular the Glencoul Thrust can be seen in a much wider perspective (see Photos w3.2 and w3.3).

From that viewpoint, the general location of the major Moine Thrust can be discerned way beyond Loch Glencoul and Loch na Gainmhich. This has pushed Moine Group rocks on top of Cambrian quartzite and ancient gneiss. The Glencoul Thrust is much easier to see and has shoved ancient gneiss on top of the Cambrian quartzite. Less evident is the Ben More Thrust (see Photo w4.9) which lies in between the Moine and the Glencoul Thrusts. These are all large-scale 'sheet thrusts', carrying a large sheet-like fold of the rock across the top of other rock. The Moine Thrust is undoubtedly the longest, as the other two only outcrop in Assynt.

Photo 5.2 + Diagram 5.4
The classic view of the Glencoul Thrust.

The western end of the Moine Thrust Zone is less clear cut; it lies roughly at the boundary between two Cambrian rocks (the slightly older quartzite and the slightly younger limestone; see Chapter 4). Some siltstone and sandstone strata are found between the quartzite and the limestone, and provided the weak link where thrusting has occurred.

The thrusting has in places extended into the Cambrian quartzite, and they are the rocks that have undergone the most severe imbrication. There are numerous imbricated areas all along the western boundary of the Moine Thrust Zone around Loch More in the north and between Loch Glencoul and south of Breabag.

Walks 1–4 all give excellent views of Assynt and nearby thrusts and imbrication zones, but there are many other excellent sites in the area. Some additional places to visit are suggested in the box 'Thrust scenery in Assynt'.

Leaving the Assynt area and moving southwards, there is another bulge in the Moine Thrust Zone on either side of the south-eastern end of Loch Maree, less varied than the Assynt bulge, but with some contradictory relationships between the younger quartzite and the older gneiss and sandstone. The juxtaposition of quartzite and sandstone on adjacent mountains, Meall a' Ghuibhuis and Ruadh stac Beag, has already been mentioned. An even more complex set of relationships is found adjacent to Slioch on Beinn a' Mhuinidh (see Walk 5 and Photo 2.8).

On Slioch itself the order of the rocks is as one would expect: younger Torridonian sandstone sits on top of an 'exhumed' valley landscape carved into ancient gneiss. Across the trench-like valley of Gleann Bianasdail however, on the slope up towards the summit of Beinn a' Mhuinidh, we encounter imbricated Cambrian quartzites on the lower reaches. On top of that lie ancient gneiss which had been pushed forwards, before the great Moine Thrust, creating another complex bulge or window in the area between Loch Maree and Loch Carron. The thrusting here has resulted in imbricated quartzites and the upside-down mountains such as Meall a' Ghuibhuis and Beinn a' Mhuinidh.

Similar confounding combinations of rock can be found elsewhere in the same area. Beinn Eighe has plenty of Cambrian quartzite on top of Torridonian sandstone; like the quartzite of Assynt it is heavily imbricated. The area southeast of Beinn Eighe has also been heavily imbricated (see Diagram 5.5), but here the thrusting has involved the Torridonian sandstone and the ancient gneiss. For example, the two popular adjacent peaks An Ruadh Stac and Maol Chean Dearg have a quartz top sitting on Torridonian sandstone and a Torridonian topping on quartzite, respectively (see Diagram 5.5). The thrusting has also produced some magnificent scenery in this area; these hills display their geology in proud and bold lines (see Photo 4.1).

There is more superb scenery to the east where Sgorr Ruadh and Beinn Liath Mhor also mix quartzite and sandstone in complex imbricated layers. To the southeast, ancient gneiss and Cambrian limestone are thrust into unnatural relationship on the flanks of Sgurr a' Gharaidh (see Walk 7 and Photo w7.4).

Even from this brief account it is clear that the Moine Thrust Zone is a complex phenomenon with major thrusts merging into areas of imbrication, and there are many more intricacies associated with thrusting than I have attempted to deal with. As a result, the Moine Thrust Zone presents us with a stunning array of landscapes which tell us something about their geological history. Ironically, despite being the biggest single thrust of the whole zone, the Moine Thrust is a less scenically interesting feature. It can be appreciated both close up and from a wider perspective at Knockan Crag in Assynt (see box 'Thrust scenery in Assynt').

Thrusting is a key part of the Cambrian landscape of northwest Scotland. Unravelling the dizzying variety of what sits on top of what and where gives these hills a unique geological interest, along with their compelling scenery and satisfying walking.

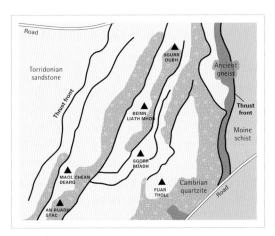

Diagram 5.5 | Geological map of Maol Chean Dearg area. (The black lines in the diagram represent lines of imbrication thrust).

Photo 5.3 | Moine Thrust at Knockan Crag; older Moine Group rocks thrust on top of younger Cambrian rocks.

Thrust scenery in Assynt

The Assynt area is a Mecca for geologists. The quality and variety of relationships between different rocks in this complex thrust zone is what draws numerous geologists and geology students to make the long trek north to this area. Knockan Crag gives a nice view of the Moine Thrust itself (see Photo 5.3), but the wider Assynt bulge in the Moine Thrust Zone provides plenty of examples of more complex thrusting patterns, including areas of intense 'imbrication'.

The Knockan Crag visitor centre is well worth a visit for access to the Moine Thrust, for its 'interpretative' material and for the short trail round several interesting features. The Moine Thrust is seen close-up at several exposures, one well provided with interpretative material (including a large wooden hand in case the distinctly different rock types do not provide sufficiently forceful indication). Various other exposures display a variety of rocks, including a rock known as 'mylonite'. These are rocks found at or close to the contact between the thrusting layers of rock and where the minerals have undergone plastic deformation. The minerals were stretched longwise by the tension between the forces thrusting the rocks forward and the forces of resistance and friction (see Photo 5.4).

It is worth walking to the highest point of the trail and then stepping over the fence to reach a slightly higher viewpoint a short distance east. You will be rewarded with a wide view of the Moine landscape to the north and east as well as a view of the more complex Assynt bulge to the north (see Photo 6.3).

Going north from Knockan Crag on the main road, the imbricated thrust planes of the Cambrian quartzite (see main text of this chapter) are easily observed on Breabag (Walk 4); the same walk also offers a fine view of the Ben More Thrust which brings ancient gneiss on top of Cambrian quartzite (see Photo w4.8). More imbricated thrusts can be seen in the limestone crags above the caves in Caves valley on the route in and out of Walk 4. Another spectacular view of thrusts is seen from the summit ridge between Conival and Ben More Assynt, looking north over Coire a' Mhadaidh to the crags of Na Tuadhan on the left. The Ben More Thrust passes here, rising from lower right to upper left at the bealach before Na Tuadhan, with ancient gneiss below the thrust and Cambrian Period quartzites above it in imbricated piles. The folds associated with imbrication are clearest where they outcrop as a crest-like top to the crags.

Heading further north between the Caves valley and Traligill valley, a superb exposure of thrusting is seen on the limestone crags on the eastern side of the road. As mentioned in the previous chapter, those who take the short walk into the Traligill valley (or the longer walk via that valley up onto Conival and Ben More Assynt) will pass a feature that combines the topic of thrusts and that of limestone's unusual drainage system (see Chapter 4). A thrust zone where one layer of dark-coloured limestone has been thrust on top of another layer of light-coloured limestone is distinctly visible (see Photo 5.5). The thrust leads up to the Lower Traligill Cave which is the point (in all but very wet weather) where the burn draining the valley disappears underground into the limestone.

The thrust plane gives the water easy access into the limestone. This is what gives some geological background knowledge some of its greatest value in the hills when you combine different components of the landscape into an overall explanation of what can be seen on the ground.

Photo 5.4 | Mylonite (stretched minerals giving a streaky appearance to the rock close to the Moine Thrust), Knockan Crag.

Photo 5.5 | Thrust plane exposed in Cambrian limestone in Traligill valley, forming a channel for water to drain into the rock.

CHAPTER 6

Metamorphic Menu

A' Mhoine is the Gaelic name for the bleak wilderness located on a blunt peninsula on the northern coast, between Loch Eriboll to the west and the Kyle of Tongue to the east. A' Mhoine rather aptly translates as 'peat bog'. The soggy peninsula merges slowly into higher ground to its south where it is bounded by Ben Hope, the northernmost of the Munros.

Geologists have however purloined and bastardised the name, anglicising it as the Moine. They've also stretched its geographical extent way beyond Ben Hope, to encompass the whole of the area between the Highland Thrust Zone and the Great Glen (this area is also known as the Northern Highlands). The rocks of the area are labelled the 'Moine Supergroup' by geologists, and the whole area is also called the Northern Highlands Terrane. In effect, the 'Moine', the 'Northern Highlands' and the 'Northern Highlands Terrane' are rough synonyms for the same area; similarly, the 'Moine rocks' and the Moine Supergroup are synonyms for the rocks found within that area.

In older maps and books the Moine rocks included some found south of the Great Glen, but this classification is no longer used by many geologists and the label is now generally applied only to rocks north of the Great Glen.

The western boundary of the Moine rocks lies along the line of the Moine Thrust (see Chapter 5). As we saw in the previous chapter, the Moine rocks have been carried several tens of kilometres from the southeast to lie above both younger and older rocks. There are in fact more thrusts further to the east within the Moine. We saw in the previous chapter that the oldest thrusts in thrust zones were those closest to the colliding plate boundaries. In the case of the Highlands, these more easterly thrusts are older than the Moine Thrust as the pressures of continental collision came from the southeast.

However, these thrusts are far less studied than the Moine Thrust and Moine Thrust Zone. The vast size of the Northern Highlands, where great swathes are hidden beneath blankets of peat and vegetation combined with the fact that much of it is 1–2 days' walk from roads, means that the rocks have been mapped in far less detail than those of the comparatively more accessible rock exposures of Assynt. The evidence for these older thrusts is found in scattered locations so geologists still dispute the details, arguing for example over whether or not a section of thrust identified in the north of the Moine is connected with one or another section of thrust found in the south of the region.

Geologists divide the Moine Supergroup into three subordinate rock 'groups': the Morar, Glenfinnan and Loch Eil. The hillwalker need not worry too much about this as it is a rather specialist pursuit. To put it in unforgiving geological jargon, the latest academic geology guide to the Moine notes that "there still remains a lack of consensus concerning the correlations of certain tectonostratigraphic units and structures, and the nature of the Neoproterozoic evolution". In other words, geologists are still debating the origin of the rocks and the tectonic processes that metamorphosed, deformed and thrust them into their present condition.

The three groups are differentiated on the basis of different stages of deposition of sediments in 'extensional basins' as the continental crust was being stretched. It is however increasingly recognised that the three rock groups also have different tectonic histories, hence the use of the rather unlovely term 'tectonostratigraphic units'. This essentially means that the Moine is subdivided into thrust sheets. These different thrust sheets by and large correlate with the three rock groups of the Morar, Glenfinnan and Loch Eil.

To understand how this happened, we need to return to before the thrusting began to discover how the thrusted rocks were originally created. They started life as sedimentary rock formed from sand, silt and mud sediments dumped in slowly deepening basins, created during stretching of the continental plate. The deepening of the basins over millions of years provided space for the accumulation of several thousand metres of sedimentary rock. This dumping of material into the basins and its transformation into solid sedimentary rock took place from about 1 billion to 870 million years ago.

Eventually the eons of extension and sedimentation drew to a close and the continental plate was compressed during continental collision between 870 and 740 million years ago, and then in the Caledonian Orogeny between 490 and 390 million year ago. During phases within these mountain-building episodes, the sedimentary rocks were subject to great heat and pressure. This led to the 'metamorphosis' and 'deformation' of the sedimentary rocks.

The thrusting also occurred during these periods of continental collision. The Sgurr Beag Thrust was probably first set in motion around 820–725 million years ago. Some 250 million years later, the Sgurr Beag Thrust was again set into action and the Naver Thrust was created. The Moine Thrust and the imbricated Moine Thrust Zone (see Chapter 5) then came into being, dating from between 430 and 390 million years ago.

The thrusting in the Moine has not produced the same complex and convoluted scenery as in the Moine Thrust Zone. Large-scale deformation has however left its mark on the land-scape, as well as on a small scale in outcrops and pebbles of metamorphic rock.

It was during these bouts of continental collision that the Hebridean Terrane to the northwest (see Chapter 2), the Northern Highlands Terrane in the middle and the Grampian Terrane (see Chapter 7) to the south were slotted into their present configuration. The ter-ranes originally developed some distance from each other along the margins of a great chunk of continental plate known to geologists as Laurentia. Its scissor-like collision with two other chunks of continental plate, Avalonia and Baltica, led to the Scottish terranes being pushed sideways into alignment with each other.

The geological history of the Northern Highlands illustrates the gross tectonic forces that create the basic landscape. Heat and pressure change the crystals within the rocks, deform the structure of the rocks, squeeze it into gigantic folds that can be thrust horizontally over scores of kilometres and slide big chunks of it sideways, creating new configurations of terranes.

Having looked at thrusting in the previous chapter and the first part of this chapter, we can now turn our attention to another key feature of mountain building: metamorphism. Metamorphism transforms existing rocks through a process known as 'solid-state recrystal-lisation'. The rock does not melt, but is put under very great heat and pressure for a sustained period of time. Recrystallisation occurs when the rock reaches between one-third and one-half of its melting temperature. The melting point of a rock depends on its chemical nature and on the particular mix of temperature and pressure. Most metamorphic reactions occur at temperatures between 100 and 850°C. These conditions are found fairly deep in crust, usually between 25 and 35km below the earth's surface.

The great pressures and temperatures found at these depths cause enormous strain on the boundaries between individual grains of crystal in the rock. Under these conditions the minerals start to exchange ions, usually along the grain boundaries. At extremes of heat and pressure, some ions can even diffuse through the middle of the crystal lattices forming the individual grains.

The result of this exchange of ions is the creation of new minerals that increasingly replace existing minerals. Fluids (including water) within the rocks aid the chemical reactions that lead to recrystallisation. The processes of recrystallisation often force the migration of the crystals into layers where the same types of crystal come together. This segregation of mineral types often results in a fairly clear 'lineation' or 'banding' appearing in the rocks. Metamorphism can affect rocks several times during their lifetime, such as has happened to the ancient gneiss of northwest Scotland and to the Moine rocks.

Photo 6.1 | Shiny schist, clearly layered with light- and dark-coloured bands created by the migration into like groups of minerals during recrystallisation.

Photo 6.2 | Moine schist displaying severe deformation caused by squeezing and heating of the rocks during recrystallisation.

The classification of metamorphic rocks is quite complex and there are different ways of describing them (see box 'Metamorphism'). The traditional term used for the rocks of the Moine is 'schist', although other names are increasingly used in academic publications. For geologists, the key characteristic of schist is that it is banded or layered and that it splits fairly easily along those bands (making it 'schistose').

For hillwalkers a useful characteristic of schist is that it is often shiny and even sparkling in the sun (see Photo 6.1). The shine comes from the flat faces of the recrystallised minerals in the rock. Crystals of a dark mineral, 'mica', are what reflect the light so effectively. The individual crystals in schist are often visible and in some cases can be up to 1–2mm in size. The reflecting mineral can appear to be metallic, but this is an optical trick; a closer look with strong reading glasses or a hand lens usually allows you to see the dark face of the mica crystals. The shine is partly dependent on how recently the rock has been broken. Well-weathered and lichen-covered schists on a dull day may hardly shine at all, while a fresh face in bright sunshine may reflect the light like finely crumpled tin foil.

Severe deformation caused by compression of the rocks during continental collision is widely seen in the Moine schists (see Photos 6.2, w8.1 and w8.4). This is 'plastic' or 'ductile' deformation, rather than 'brittle' deformation. The dominance of plastic deformation (and the absence of brittle deformation) is another indication that the rocks were subject to heat and pressure at considerable depth, well out of range of the upper zones where brittle deformation is possible (see box 'Deformation' in Chapter 7).

Erosion has however removed great masses of overlying rock from the original massive folds, meaning that geologists have had to work out how the greater patterns extended into now eroded-away rock. These interpretations are based on analysis of ground outcrops of the rocks and working out a three-dimensional picture of existing and formerly existing rocks. There are as many projected patterns as there are geologists who have attempted an analysis.

Compared to the Grampian Terrane, the Northern Highlands Terrane includes few igneous rocks. A basaltic intrusion, metamorphosed to a rock type known as 'amphibolite', gives Ben Hope its sharp scarp slope (see Photo 1.2). There are also scattered granite intrusions pushed up into the developing sedimentary rock of the Glenfinnan and Loch Eil groups about 870 million years ago, but the overall contribution to the scenery of volcanic rock is limited.

The Moine landscape is pretty varied. The scenery is fairly restrained in places with smooth, rounded hill tops stretching off into the distance such as in the northern part of the region (for example east of Assynt; see Photo 6.3). However, glacial action has carved highly impressive chunks out of the mountains in the form of corries and deep glens, ensuring plenty of scenic charm and often emphasising the overall large-scale deformation tilt of the rocks (see Photo 1.2). Sgurr Mor, the highest point in the Moine region at 1110m, is a good, pointed summit which is fairly easy to climb from Loch Droma near Ullapool (see Photo 6.4). Coire Ghranda below Beinn Dearg (one of the area's most popular mountains) provides a fine example of the power of glacial carving and its role in creating the scenery. Like Sgurr Mor, Beinn Dearg is fairly easy to access from near Ullapool.

Photo 6.3 | Moine landscape viewed from above Knockan Crag.

Photo 6.4 | Sgurr Mor, the highest point in the Moine landscape.

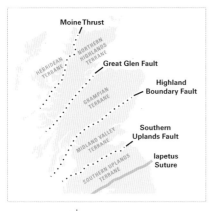

Diagram 6.1 | Terranes forming Scotland.

This popular mountain area sits at the centre of a very large-scale 'antiform' and 'synform', or a dome-like and basin-like fold, respectively (see Diagram 7.1). This is part of the very large-scale deformation of the rocks during metamorphosis and squeezing. The rocks can be seen tilting from upper left to lower right in Photo 6.4, with the lines of snow below the col to the left of the summit bringing out this feature. The anticline is centred on the left of the photo, while the corresponding syncline is centred just out of the picture to its right.

Another superb area for easy access to the Moine mountains is around Glen Shiel (see Photo 6.5), including the Five Sisters of Kintail. It is possible to see the wider picture here and recognise the tilt of the rocks and you will also find plenty of deformed boulders and pebbles (see Walk 8). The Moine also stretches as far as Ardnamurchan, the western-most point on the British mainland. The Moine is a vast and varied landscape of often intensely deformed metamorphic rock from the Moine Thrust to the Great Glen, offering us an insight into the violent forces which brought it into being.

Photo 6.5 | The North Cluanie ridge seen from Sgurr Mhic Bharraich.

Metamorphism

Banding is quite common in those metamorphic rocks known as 'slate', 'schist' and 'gneiss'. Slate is a very low grade of metamorphic rock produced by the high pressure but not very high temperatures, typical of subduction zones. In these conditions, the flat 'platy' mineral grains are pressed into alignment. This allows the rock to split easily along the lines or 'cleavage planes'.

Schist is higher up the metamorphic scale and is produced by higher temperatures and pressures, but it shares the ability of slate to split easily along the banding produced by metamorphism. The defining characteristic of schist is indeed its 'schistosity' or ability to split, even if it doesn't split as cleanly and as thinly as slate.

Gneiss is another notch up on the scale. It too is banded, but it has undergone a still greater degree of pressure and yet higher temperatures. Although banded, the crystals are also bonded more forcefully meaning that gneiss does not split along the banding.

The next category on the scale is 'migmatite'; it is produced by very hot conditions and involves a partial melt of the rock. The melting is partial as only those minerals with a relatively low melting point reach the necessary temperature, while those with a higher melting point remain solid.

All these rock types are actually part of a continuum and, as has often been said, 'one geologist's schist is another geologist's gneiss'. Indeed, the process of 'diagenesis' (the chemical changes and compaction that transform loose sediment into solid rock) can be included with metamorphosis; it is the first step in the whole process of changes that can affect the minerals that come together to form rocks.

Not all metamorphic rocks are banded; for example, quartzite doesn't show any banding. It is very high in quartz (80% or more) so there are not enough different types of crystals in the metamorphosed rock to migrate into bands. An interlocking mosaic of quartz crystals is instead formed when the individual sand grains in the sandstone are recrystallised, along with the cementing material.

There are other methods of categorising metamorphic rocks and quite different naming conventions are also in use. The 'slate/schist/gneiss' grading is based on what geologists call the 'texture' of the rock. Other methods of classification and associated terms are increasingly being used, such as 'psammite' or 'meta-psammite' (indicating that it was originally a sandstone) and 'pellite' or 'meta-pellite' (indicating that it was originally a mudstone). Meta-psammite is the dominant rock type in the Moine Supergroup, although meta-pellite and quartzite are also common.

'Slate' is now officially to be called 'slaty meta-mudstone' or 'slaty meta-siltstone' (depending on whether the 'protolith' or original sedimentary rock was mudstone or siltstone, respectively). In this book I have however stuck with the more familiar names (but watch out for these terms appearing in newer geology maps and academic publications).

One illustration of the difficulties and contradictions is a recent British Geological Survey publication on the new system of metamorphic rock classifications (for sufferers of insomnia, freely downloadable from the BGS website). Certain low-grade metamorphic rocks, it says, "have been traditionally referred to as greenschists", but "many such rocks are neither green nor schistose". No wonder geology is seen as a difficult subject!

The great bulk of metamorphic rocks in the Highlands are the product of what geologists call 'regional' metamorphism, generated by tectonic collisions that affect considerable areas. Under such conditions, recrystallisation is often associated with some form of 'deformation' of the rocks due to the strain exerted by plate collision (see box 'Deformation' in Chapter 7).

There are other causes of metamorphism, such as 'contact' metamorphism. This is the result of hot molten magma being intruded into rocks as it moves towards the earth's surface. If the magma doesn't make it all the way and cools down as an intrusion, it can 'bake' the surrounding rock to a greater or lesser extent. This is common around large 'dykes' and 'sills' as well as much larger blobs or 'plutons' (usually of granite).

CHAPTER 7

Dalradian Deformation

The area between the Great Glen and the Highland Boundary Fault, known to geologists as the Grampian Terrane, is home to some of the most fantastic scenery in Britain. The Grampian Highlands contains Ben Nevis, the Cairngorms, the ridges of Glen Coe, Ben Lomond and many other immensely popular peaks.

In this region the mountain ridges often stick out like ribs. It is perhaps not surprising that during the 16th and 17th centuries, when 'geology' was a proto-science, it was commonly believed that mountain ranges were the surface expressions of the skeleton that held the earth together. Today we think differently, seeing mountain ranges as the product of colliding continental plates. Rather than being the earth's supporting structural skeleton, mountain ranges are in fact mere wrinkles on its skin and temporary ones at that.

The uplands of the Scottish Highlands do not strictly meet the geomorphologist's definition of 'mountains', a label which applies only if the earthly swelling is greater than 2,000m above mean sea level. In the Highlands we have just the eroded remains of a once great mountain range. Age has not deepened this old wrinkled zone, but seen it slowly rubbed away.

Today the stumps of that once massive mountain range expose the deep interior of the crust. This allows us to see 'inside' those ancient mountains, to peer down into the hot, dense depths of the crust where deformation and metamorphism took place. Erosion has 'exhumed' these depths for us to observe the evidence of their origin and intervening history. The Grampian Terrane is a superb place for the study of ancient mountains, whatever their nominal status. As we see in this and the following two chapters, these bony mountain stumps provide stunning scenery in which to walk or climb while pondering the deep origins of the landscape.

There is more geological variety in the rocks of the 'Grampian Highlands' than in the Northern Highlands. One distinct difference between the Northern Highlands Terrane and the Grampian Terrane is the extent of igneous rocks within the area. The Moine has but few igneous intrusions, while in the Grampians there are many. Most of these intrusions are quite limited in size, but there are also pretty large ones. The Cairngorms is one well-known granite area and Ben Nevis is another; we will look at these areas in Chapters 8 and 9 respectively.

There are also outcrops of 'extrusive' igneous rock (lavas and 'pyroclastic' eruptions), especially around Glencoe, and these will also come under scrutiny in Chapter 9. In this chapter we will concentrate on the metamorphic rocks of the Grampian Highlands, otherwise known as the 'Dalradian Supergroup'.

Geologists divide the Dalradian Supergroup into four groups: the Grampian, Appin, Argyll and Southern Highland groups. Each group represents a cycle of crustal subsidence leading to the development of a basin which was invaded by the sea. Sediment dumped into the sea was slowly transformed into sandstone, siltstone and mudstone. The rocks were originally laid down from about 790 to 525 million years ago. This latter date brings us back within the early Cambrian, so the Dalradian rocks are older than the Cambrian quartzites and limestones that we looked at in the Moine Thrust Zone (see Chapter 5).

Deposition of sediment in subsiding basins continued for all those millions and millions of years at a time when the continental crust was being stretched by the rifting and thinning of the plate. There were also episodes of continental collision, leading to repeated phases of metamorphosis, deformation and mountain building.

In general, the rocks of the Dalradian Supergroup have experienced less extensive metamorphosis than those of the Moine. However, the Dalradian Supergroup rocks have been subject to very intense 'plastic' or 'ductile' deformation (see box 'Deformation' in this chapter).

The metamorphic rocks are mainly schists and quartzites and are known to geologists as the 'Dalradian Supergroup'. Schist is quite a shiny rock with light reflected from crystals which are often large enough to be seen by the naked eye (or in more detail with strong reading glasses or a hand lens; see Photo 7.1). The defining characteristic of schist is its layered structure as different minerals arrange themselves into bands during metamorphosis (when the minerals

Photo 7.1 | Dalradian Supergroup schist, Grampian Highlands.

Photo 7.2 | Dalradian Supergroup quartzite, Grampian Highlands.

Photo 7.3 | Deformation folds on a large scale, Grey Corries (viewed from Aonach Beag).

Photo 7.4 | Deformation folds on a large scale, Mamores (viewed from Aonach Beag).

in the original rock do not melt but are recrystallised). The rock often splits easily along these lines, giving it 'schistosity'. The original rocks were sandstone or siltstone (see Chapter 6).

Unlike the sedimentary Cambrian quartzite encountered in the northwest and the Moine Thrust Zone, the Dalradian quartzite is a metamorphic rock which has undergone recrystallisation and it was originally a quartz-rich sandstone. By definition, quartzite contains over 80% quartz (silica). It doesn't form into banding like schist or have shiny patches; instead, quartzite has a milky texture (see Photo 7.2). It splits unevenly with quite sharp edges, so it is often unpleasant to walk on and causes a lot of wear and tear to walkers' boots.

The most remarkable feature of the hills built out of both quartzite and schist in the Grampians is the extent of the deformation to be seen in the outcrops. In the case of the schists, the deformation can be seen at both the miniature and mega-scale in small hand samples of rock as well as from a distance looking at the wider scenery. The quartzite has been folded into great curves which are visible in the Grey Corries (Photo 7.3) and Mamores (Photo 7.4) ranges, offering some of the most dramatic mountain scenery of the Highlands.

These intense 'plastic' or 'ductile' deformations take place low down in the crust (25–35km depth) during continental collision. The folds shown in Photos 7.3 and 7.4 illustrate how the present-day rocks were part of massive 'nappes' or great overfolds in the rock strata (see Diagram 5.1). The overlying layers have now been eroded away, but geologists have attempted to visualise them by analysing the parts that can be mapped on the ground.

The fold shown in Photos 7.3 and 7.4 are exceptional examples; such clear folds are not usually readily visible. However, a significant tilt in the rock strata is often quite easy to see on the hillsides. These tilted strata represent what is left of massive folds and nappes, created by plastic deformation as the continents collided and compressed the rocks. The chunk of continental plate in this area may have been squeezed to about one-thirtieth of its original length as the rocks were folded, broken and piled up.

Deformation in the schist can be seen at both the large and small scales, and there are innumerable places where you will encounter intensely folded boulders and pebbles (see Photos w17.4 and w18.2). These smaller-scale folds show the same folding pattern as larger folds, so are a fractal pattern. This can be seen on Walk 17 along the Meall nan Tarmachan ridge (see Photos w17.2 and w17.3), where patches of small outcrops show how the deformation pattern replicates the overall tilt of the whole ridge.

The structure of the Grampian Highlands is extremely complex with a number of 'megafolds', including complete overturning of rock layers. The severe folding in the Mamores and Grey Corries is part of a substantial 'synform' or downwards folding of the rocks known as the Stob Ban synform, which runs from Stob Ban to the northeast for several kilometres. The terms 'synform' and 'antiform' are similar to the terms 'syncline' and 'anticline'; the latter terms apply to sedimentary rock where the original sedimentary bedding can be seen, while the former terms apply to rocks which have been recrystallised and deformed and the original bedding destroyed (see Diagram 7.1).

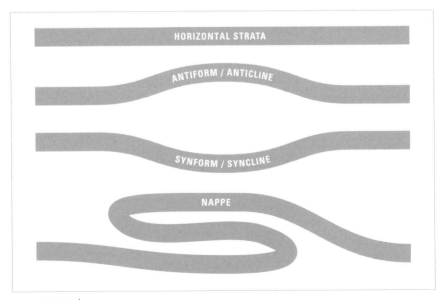

Diagram 7.1 | Rock deformation folds.

The southern limits of the Grampians are marked by a sharp downturn in the rocks as they dip downwards, cut off only at the Highlands Boundary Fault. This fault zone features its own geological contortions, the result of being squeezed between the Grampian Highlands and the Midlands Valley area of Scotland during the continental collision.

The Highland Boundary Fault marks the location where the Grampian Terrane meets the Central Lowlands Terrane. It is an intense mix of different rocks types in about ten slivers of crust. The rocks include metamorphic 'serpentine', lavas and sedimentary rock. Some of the rocks were parts of the ocean crust which escaped subduction and were caught up in an 'accretionary zone', where an oceanic and a continental plate collided.

Having looked at the metamorphic rocks of the Grampians, we now need to bring into the picture a series of igneous events that affected the Grampian Terrane and which occurred during the collision of continents. We will deal with some of the biggest events (and the most important scenically) in the following two chapters, but here is it necessary to briefly refer to a mass of smaller events which intruded molten rock into the metamorphic rocks from below.

These molten rock intrusions are long sheets of rock formed from the cooling of molten magma within the existing rock, generally known as 'dykes' and 'sills'. A sill is a horizontal or near-horizontal sheet and dykes are more or less vertical. Both are created by molten magma forcing its way into faults and/or rock boundaries, creating space for a sheet of the molten matter to be injected. Some of the intrusions were the source of magma that erupted at the surface while others did not reach the surface. If the overlying rocks have been eroded away, the dyke or sill is usually exposed at the surface as a more or less linear feature although often broken and somewhat displaced by movement along faults.

Photo 7.5 | Reddish scree betrays the location of an intrusion from a distance (Creag Meagaidh).

Photo 7.6

A particularly sharp boundary between an intrusion (reddish rocks) and surrounding schist (greyish rocks); north Glencoe ridge.

Some dykes and sills are made of granitic material and have a reddish tinge (see Photos 7.5, 7.6, w16.3 and w16.4). These intrusions are quite easy to spot where they are exposed within the greyish outcrops of schist, and can be seen at a distance as well as close up. Not all intrusions are highlighted by a nice conspicuous splash of red, however; sometimes a careful examination of the changing rocks around you is required.

Dykes can range in size from a few centimetres to a few metres. One substantial dyke is encountered on Walk 17 below the Meall nan Tarmachan ridge. The dyke is about 2km long and forms a very distinctive feature, running across the lower southern flank of the ridge forming the lip of a glacial corrie. The rock is noticeably very different from the surrounding schists which are well-layered, forming innumerable rock ledges and outcrops as well as being covered in lichen and vegetation. On the other hand, the igneous rock is 'massive' (a technical term for not displaying a lineation) broken only by irregular jointing. It is very 'clean-looking', well-weathered for sure, but a fairly uniform grey and with large exposed patches free of vegetation. The differences are reflected in the wider scenery, with the complex, craggy slopes of the schist contrasting strongly with the solid cliff of igneous rock (see Photos w17.6 and w17.7).

In the next two chapters we will look at some of the more major igneous events that affected the Grampian Terrane and produced the scenery of present-day Cairngorms, Ben Nevis and Glen Coe.

Deformation

At shallow levels in the crust 'brittle deformation' (or cracking of the rocks) predominates, but at great depths 'plastic' or 'ductile' deformation takes over and the crystals in the rock stretch rather than break. The thrusting seen in the Highlands (see Chapter 5) occurs at a transitional depth where both brittle and plastic deformation occur.

At very great depths rocks can be transformed into a ductile state and deformed into small, medium and large folds. The deformation takes place when the 'yield strength' of the material is exceeded by the 'gliding motions' of large numbers of defects in the crystal lattice of minerals making up the rock. The result is 'ductile' or 'plastic' deformation (rather than 'brittle' deformation or fracturing of the rock).

Brittle deformation is more likely if the compression pressure is applied rapidly. If pressure is applied for long periods of time and at a suitable heat, however, then ductile deformation can take place. Deformation is closely linked to metamorphic change. Existing grains are destroyed to one extent or another during metamorphosis, while new grains grow. In plastic deformation the grains may be stretched without breaking, allowing movement to take place.

Deformation may well kick-start metamorphic change by creating the conditions needed to set off the process of recrystallisation on the boundaries of crystal grains. This is because deformation changes the shape of the individual crystals within the rock by moving individual ions or packets of ions in a systematic way. Deformation strains the existing crystals so they are replaced by crystals which are not strained in the deformed state. All minerals contain defects, such as incorrectly positioned or missing atoms, and when a grain is stressed the defects can move through the crystal lattice generating new defects. Grains become smaller but elongated, meaning that the rock retains its coherence during ductile deformation (i.e. it does not fracture or break).

Plastic deformation also explains two wider features of tectonics. First, it is plastic flow of the earth's mantle rocks in great convection currents which transfers heat from the earth's core towards its surface and drives the movement of the tectonic plates. Second, plastic deformation of the mantle is what allows the continental crust to thicken downwards during mountain building (similarly, the mantle accommodates the weight of great accumulations of ice during cold periods by plastic deformation).

Photo 7.7 | Deformation in Moine schist

CHAPTER 8

Grampian Granite

About 600 million years ago, continental collision led to volcanoes breaking through to the surface of the earth and, in much greater quantities, the intrusion of molten 'magma' into rocks towards the base of the plate. This magma either cooled down slowly low in the crust to form large masses ('plutons') or rose higher to form 'dykes' and 'sills' intruded into the metamorphic rocks. More tectonic and volcanic activity took place during the destruction of the Iapetus Ocean, squeezed out of existence by the subsequent collision of Laurentia with Avalonia and Baltica. This tectonic activity reached its maximum extent about 470 million years ago and again about 400 million years ago.

The Northern Highlands (see Chapter 6) and the Grampian Highlands (see Chapter 7) are both mainly areas of metamorphic schists, although there are other rocks. In the Grampians in particular there are several significant outcrops of an intrusive rock known as 'granite'.

Like limestone, slate and marble, granite is one of those rock types which everyone has heard of. Granite is a very tough rock and is a watchword for strength and stability. It is created when the rocks towards the bottom of a continental plate melt to become molten magma. This is most likely to occur either when two continental plates collide and thicken the plate (causing it to extend downwards as well as upwards) or when an oceanic plate subducts below a continental plate (water dragged down by the subducting plate lowers the temperature at which the base of the continental plate melts).

Diagram 8.1
Igneous rock
classification.

	Rhyolitic	Dacitic	Andesitic	Basaltic
Extrusive	Tuffs (pyroclastic)			
				Lavas (effusive)
Intrusive:				
fine grain	rhyolite	dacite	andesite	basalt
medium	microgranite	microgranodiorite	diorite	dolerite
large grain	granite	granodiorite	trachyandesite	gabbro

Two defining characteristics of granite are: first, it contains a high proportion (over 60%) of the mineral known as 'silica' (which is a major component of continental crust) and second, it has cooled quite slowly deep underground so that it contains large crystals (distinguishable by the naked eye). Diagram 8.1 shows how granite relates to other igneous rocks with a high proportion of silica. Granitic (or 'rhyolitic') rocks are formed from recycled continental plate.

The Grampian granites, which are found in the Highlands between the Great Glen and the Highland Boundary Fault, are mainly the product of the great forces generated by the suduction of an oceanic plate under a continental plate. This occurred during early phases of the 'Caledonian Orogeny' or mountain-building episode, when the continents' island arcs and continental shelves began to collide. These granites are intimately connected with some of the Scottish Highlands best-known mountain scenery: Ben Nevis, the Cairngorms, the Monadhliath massif and the Ben Cruachan massif. Ben Nevis is actually a mix of granite and rocks formed from erupted volcanic lava. In this chapter we will look in a little detail at the granite of Cairngorms, both for its own interest and as a proxy for the other Grampian granites. The granites of Ben Nevis are discussed in the next chapter.

The Cairngorms is one of the most popular Highland landscapes. It not only attracts many walkers and mountaineers but, if there is snow in winter, lots of skiers as well. The area around the summit known as Cairn Gorm is badly spoilt by the ski infrastructure, but otherwise the Cairngorms form a large and undeveloped upland plateau and remain one of the biggest road-free areas in Britain. The massif forms a broad dome stretching about 30km from east to west and 10–20km from north to south, covering some 365km².

The mountains are correspondingly bulky. At 1,309m, Ben Macdui is Scotland's second-highest mountain; indeed, the Cairngorms massif is home to four out of five of the highest mountains in Britain. It has more area above 900m than anywhere else in Britain with vast open skies, great expanses of rolling hills and spectacularly deep corries and glacial valleys.

Photo 8.1 |
View east from
Cairn Toul.

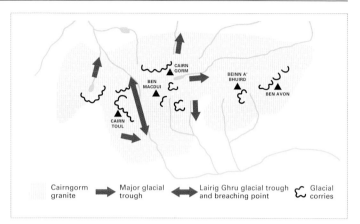

Diagram 8.2

The Cairngorm granite outcrop.

▨ Cairngorm granite	➡ Major glacial trough
⟷ Lairig Ghru glacial trough and breaching point	∿ Glacial corries

The scenery of the Cairngorms is subtly different between the eastern and western areas (see Diagram 8.2). The western parts have been cut into by deep glacial troughs such as Lairig Ghru, upper Glen Avon and Glen Derry, and there are many impressive corries. In contrast, the eastern section has only one major trough (Slochd Mor) and just a couple of clusters of corries on Ben Avon and Beinn a' Bhuird.

There are other differences between the various upland areas which the observant hillwalker may notice. Most of the upland areas are covered by a mix of grass and boulders ('block fields') but there are a couple of areas, Moine Mor and Moine Bhealaidh, which are smothered in thick layers of peat. The overall impression of the Cairngorms from most places on the upland plateau is of a gently undulating landscape interrupted only by a few deep incisions and crags. Winds blow fiercely across the summits whatever the season. Snow lies on the ground in a few places the whole year around (summer melting of the snow in An Garbh Coire occurred only three times during the 20th century).

The present-day Cairngorms granite outcrop has a gently domed central mass with steep sides. This is thought to represent the original shape of the 'pluton' or mass of molten granite that originated from very deep underground (perhaps as deep as 30km) about 430 million years ago. The molten magma then rose to about 6–8km below the surface, forcing out a space into which it could collect and where it finally cooled and solidified into granite. The depth of the base of the granite pluton today is unknown, but it certainly reaches several kilometres.

By definition, granite contains a high proportion of silica. When it first became molten magma it was probably chemically 'primitive', or pure, with a very high proportion of silica. As the magma rose upwards it evolved chemically, and the nature of that evolution varied with place to place within the pluton. As a result, the Cairngorm granite is far from homogenous. It displays a variety of characteristics, such as a grain size within the range 2–10mm with some patches qualifying as 'microgranite' rather than 'granite' (see Diagram 8.1) The easiest characteristics for the hillwalker to spot are differences in colour (from grey to pink), the nature and extent of 'jointing' and the size of the mineral grains (crystals) visible in the rocks (see Photos 8.2 and 8.3). These features represent different levels of chemical alteration in different parts of the pluton.

Some of the chemical changes occurred as the molten magma pushed its way upwards and melted the adjoining 'wall' and 'roof' rocks, for example. These melted rocks would have been incorporated into the granite, adjusting its chemical structure.

Photo 8.2 + 8.3

Pink and grey granite in the Cairngorms.

Most important of all were the different levels of water (and other 'volatiles') bound up in the molten magma. A localised high level of water could induce important chemical changes in that area as the magma cooled and crystallised. In such areas, chemically rich 'hydrothermal fluids' circulated through 'crystal boundaries', micro-fractures in the rock and pores created by mineral dissolution. The concentration of 'joints' or physical boundaries within the granite of water-rich areas was therefore much higher than for areas with less hydrothermal fluid. In water-rich areas, this led to the replacement of the original minerals and the creation of a con- nected network of pore gaps and 'veins' through which more fluids could circulate and further chemical alterations occur. This weakened the developing rock, paving the way for further fluid penetration and chemical alteration. These are what geologists refer to as 'alteration zones'.

The result of these alterations was that, when the granite was exposed to the atmosphere at the earth's surface (a few million years later after overlying rocks were eroded away), the chemically altered zones were more susceptible to atmospheric chemical weathering and to physical erosion. Photo 8.4 shows some well-jointed granite outcrop with a pinkish tinge in the deeply eroded Chalamain Gap, surrounded by a block field of boulders eroded from the slopes.

Photo 8.4 | Well-jointed pinkish granite in the Chalamain Gap.

Photo 8.5 | Heavily jointed granite at the top of the headwall of Coire an t-Sneachda, below the summit of Cairn Gorm.

The current view among geologists is that the rocks lying on top of the granite pluton eroded quite rapidly shortly after the granite was intruded and cooled. The granite was therefore exposed to the atmosphere fairly rapidly (in geological terms) by about 400–390 million years ago. The exposed granite has since been subject to intense chemical weathering and glacial erosion, being lowered in height by at least several tens of metres.

The exposed areas of the ancient alteration zones are more strongly weathered and more deeply coloured (with a pinkish tinge) than unaltered rocks. The strongly coloured granites are often found close to topographic features such as glacial troughs and corries. The 'headwalls' of corries are often very heavily jointed (see Photo 8.5), and up to 500m of granite has been eroded away from corries and troughs in these weaker areas.

There are several corries throughout the Cairngorms, occurring in clusters such as around Cairn Gorm and Cairn Toul. The big corries all share similar features and sizes, being between 900 and 1000m wide. There are also great glacial valleys such as the Lairig Ghru and Glen Avon, two deep gashes that run deep into the heart of the granite massif and provide some of its most memorable scenery. These features are all found in the zones of alteration.

Because the presence of water assists in the process of crystallisation, water-rich magmas generally result in granites with large crystals. There are patches of rock with very large crystals (known as 'pegmatite') which produce the semi-precious 'Cairngorm Stone'.

By contrast, greyer-coloured granites are more common in the outer parts of the massif and form gently undulating ground without deep dips. Similarly, the upstanding rock 'tors' which adorn a number of summits in the Cairngorms are also areas of minimal jointing and limited chemical alteration. The great rock buttresses that separate corries are also often lacking in jointing. There has been little erosion of the granite in these areas, forming the classic sweeping, muted undulating landscape of the Cairngorms upland plateau.

The tors are large blocks of granite about 10m long, rising up to 15m above the surrounding granite plateau (see Photos 8.6 and w9.5). They are rather unevenly distributed across the Cairngorm plateau; they most common in the east and central areas, with few if any in western and southern parts. The greatest grouping is found around the remote eastern area of Ben Avon. The most scenic are the 'Barns of Bynack' ('barns' being a local name for tors).

These tors are thought to represent areas of rock which are particularly resistant to weathering due to the generally lower level of jointing. Tors at all stages of development are seen in the Cairngorms, from those just beginning to be exposed to the remaining stumps of others. Despite their relative resistance, even these tors will eventually be reduced by chemical weathering and freeze/thaw action to block fields.

As mentioned above, geologists believe that the granite was exposed to the surface quite soon after it had been 'emplaced', perhaps about 390 million years ago, and has remained uncovered by other rocks since. The tough, highly resistant granite pluton therefore seems to have been unaffected by the great continental collisions that pummelled and pounded the other rocks of the Highlands, creating great mountain chains.

Indeed, it is even claimed that no major modifications of the granite has occurred since that ancient time and no new valleys been created. Tens of metres of material have been removed by chemical weathering but, in essence, it is now thought that the basic landscape we see today in the Cairngorms was established about 390 million years ago. If this theory is correct, the hillwalker who ventures out onto the Cairngorm hills is looking at a truly venerable landscape.

Photo 8.6 | Cairngorm tors, the 'Barns of Bynack', viewed from the summit plateau of Cairn Gorm.

CHAPTER 9

Igneous Intrusion

Ben Nevis and Glen Coe – two of the most celebrated scenic gems of the Highlands – are landscapes that reflect their geology. The hills of these areas are a complex mix of 'intrusive' and 'extrusive' igneous rock. Granite and other intrusive rocks feature in the story of these two special places, but so also do lavas and 'pyroclastic rocks' including some created by the hottest and most violent type of eruption. Such eruptions exploded onto the earth's surface as a very fast-moving incandescent cloud of fragments of molten magma ('ash') mixed with hot gases, and ripped away lumps of rock.

In this chapter we will look at the special conditions that led to the creation of Britain's highest mountain, Ben Nevis, as well as the area famous for containing some of the Highlands' most beautiful mountains ranges, Glen Coe. Walk 12 describes a route up and down the geology of Ben Nevis and Walk 16 traverses one of the most stunning walking routes in the Glen Coe mountains.

Ben Nevis

We will begin with the large, impressive bulk of Ben Nevis (see Photo 9.1) and its neighbours, Càrn Mor Dearg and Aonach Mor. The start of the story is rather similar to that of the Cairngorms. During the early part of the Caledonian mountain-building episode, molten magma was created by subduction of the final chunks of the Iapetus oceanic plate under the Laurentian continental plate.

A pluton of molten magma was formed under the area of present-day Ben Nevis. The magma then rose upwards, getting fairly close to the surface. There it cooled fairly slowly to form granite, a large-grained rock. It is likely that there were two quite separate 'pulses' of magma creation and subsequent journey upwards, with the second pulse being pushed up into the middle of the earlier pulse.

Photo 9.1

Ben Nevis (left) and

Càrn mor Dearg

(right), viewed from

Aonach Beag.

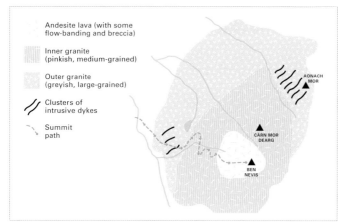

Andesite lava (with some
flow-banding and breccia)

Inner granite
(pinkish, medium-grained)

Outer granite
(greyish, large-grained)

Clusters of
intrusive dykes

Summit
path

AONACH
MOR

CÀRN MOR
DEARG

BEN
NEVIS

Diagram 9.1

Ben Nevis

geological map.

These two pulses form the 'Ben Nevis outer granite' and the 'Ben Nevis inner granite'. It should also be said that a third outer rock type known as quartz-diorite can be found mainly on the north-western limit of the outer granite, which may represent a different rate of cooling from the outer granite or an earlier pulse of magma. Little is seen of this third type of rock while out walking, so we will concentrate on the outer and inner granites.

The most obvious difference is that outer granite is rather grey in colour, while the inner granite displays a pinkish tinge. Another important difference between the two granites is that the outer is cut by scores of intrusive 'dykes'. These were created along the lines of faults by rising magma that forced its way through the outer granite as the magma rose to the surface.

While there are plenty of dykes intruded into the outer granite, its inner counterpart has no such dykes (see Diagram 9.1). This is what leads geologists to conclude that the outer and inner granites must have been created in two pulses with a time gap between them during which the dykes were intruded, and that therefore the outer granite must have been created first. It is this type of logical analysis of the rock outcrops mapped on the ground that forms the basis of much geological reasoning.

So far, so good. The history of the granite of Ben Nevis, with two quite clear time-separated pulses of magma creation, already appears to be more complicated than that of the Cairngorms. We also need to include a third event which, against all odds, has left evidence in the rock record.

The top third or so of Ben Nevis is not made of granite but of a rock known as 'andesite' (common, as the name suggests, in the present-day subduction zone of the Andes). This is a rock formed from molten magma that has erupted onto the surface, mainly in the form of flowing lava. Andesite magma has a lower proportion of silica than granite magma, and is generated at a different phase of igneous activity (see Diagram 8.1).

The area covered by the erupted andesitic lava was almost certainly much more extensive than the present-day outcrop, which is restricted in extent to its perch on top of Ben Nevis. Most of the solidified lava has now been eroded away however, and it is only by chance that we have the present-day topping of andesite on Ben Nevis. The andesite experienced a rather remarkable history, erupting onto the surface and flowing over the area including the still-molten Ben Nevis inner granite. This lava then collapsed downwards into the granite. It is estimated that the andesite must have sunk a depth of about 600m into the partially molten inner granite. It was this surrounding girdle of granite that provided refuge for the andesite on Ben Nevis, protecting it from erosion in the few hundred million years since this unlikely sounding process dumped lava into the middle of a mass of granite.

There are a couple of places where geologists have found outcrops of the metamorphic schist underlying the andesite, for example in the glen holding Allt a' Mhuilinn under Ben Nevis's overwhelmingly impressive northern flank. These tiny outcrops of schist sit on top of the granite and so must have got there in the same collapse as the andesite. This provides strong evidence for the theory of the collapse of the andesitic lava into the molten granitic magma. If no such underlying outcrops of schists had been discovered, then the story of the mega-collapse might be less convincing.

The andesitic lava shows some variety and in places contains broken lumps of rock cemented together in a 'matrix'. Such rocks are known as 'brecciated lava' (see Photos 9.2 and w12.4) and are formed when partly solidified lava cools or is given a shove by an earthquake or another eruption (or both at the same time), causing it to break up into lumps. The Ben Nevis andesite also contains some traces of a feature known as 'flow-banding'. This feature records the patterns left as the lava flowed, sometimes in a turbulent fashion, across the then surface (see Photo w12.6).

Photo 9.2

Brecciated andesite lava block near summit plateau of Ben Nevis.

The andesite is encountered at a height of about 950m on the popular Glen Nevis track, shortly after the third zigzag above the crossing of the 'Red Burn'. The boulders which litter the landscape from this point onwards are a dark grey in colour, support a variety of lichen and are irregularly 'jointed'. They are quite distinct from the pink and grey granite which are much lighter in colour, support fewer lichen species and are less jointed. The boulders form a block field that accompanies you all the way to the summit from this point (although the number of visible boulders will depend on the snow cover).

The intermixing of granite and andesite thus explains Ben Nevis's upper, lumpy pudding shape. Granite is a very tough rock and provides a large base on which the andesite sits. In the past, the granite surrounded the andesite and protected it from erosion, thus presenting us with a geological feature of great interest in the form of Britain's mightiest mountain.

Glen Coe

The great rock buttresses known as the Three Sisters of Glen Coe, along with Buachaille Etive Beag and Buachaille Etive Mor to the north, are some of the most renowned Scottish mountains. The Three Sisters provide one of the most stunning roadside views; and for walkers and climbers they offer some of the very best hillwalking and mountaineering in the Highlands. The mountains of Glen Coe are also geologically fascinating, having been created by a complex set of volcanic eruptions and, more recently, carved into magnificent shapes by glaciers.

As with Ben Nevis, it is only through geological contingency that we are fortunate enough to have the opportunity to gaze at and walk upon the scenic masterpiece of Glen Coe. The volcanic rocks have also been preserved here because they sunk down and were protected from erosion. The actual nature of the eruptions and the cause of the 'ponding' of the volcanic material, however, are quite different from those at Ben Nevis. In Glen Coe, the erupted rocks did not drop into semi-molten intrusive rocks but ponded up in what volcanologists refer to as a 'caldera'.

The Glen Coe area has long been considered the classic example of a circular caldera, its boundary marked by a circular 'ring-fault'. Quite a few volcanoes around the world have been studied in the framework of this interpretation. Recent research has however considerably modified these earlier ideas. The account provided here is based on the latest interpretation and therefore may differ from earlier geological guides.

The present view still allocates a central role to the concept of the 'caldera', but offers a more complex account of its development. A caldera is created by massive and sudden 'pyroclastic' eruptions of fragments of molten magma, hot gases and ripped away parts of the surrounding mountain. It is the hottest and most violent type of volcanic eruption. The eruption empties (fully or partly) the underground 'magma chamber', leading to the collapse of the land on top to form a large depression, usually about 10–15km in diameter.

A caldera is not the same as a 'crater', which is a comparatively much smaller depression usually found at the top of a 'volcano' at its 'vent'. Calderas are much bigger affairs, and can be hundreds of metres deep. The eruptions occur along linear features known as 'fissure vents', where a sheet of magma has forced its way up through a space between rocks either along pre-existing faults or through newly created one. The rising magma 'domes' the land upwards as it rises, and this breaks the overlying rock to create conduits leading to surface fissure vents. In the case of Glen Coe there were repeated episodes of such eruptions and land collapse, creating step by step a large depression or caldera (rather than the caldera being created in a single event, as previously thought).

The key factor determining whether a volcano erupts as flowing lava or as explosive fragments is the chemical nature of the magma. Magma formed from melted continental plate is high in silica and is very viscous (i.e. it does not flow easily), whereas magma formed from mantle rocks is low in silica and not very viscous (i.e. it flows more easily). The magmas that tend to produce lava are known as 'basaltic' and 'andesitic', while magma which produces explosive fragments is known as 'rhyolitic' (or 'granitic'; see Diagrams 8.1, 9.2 and 9.3).

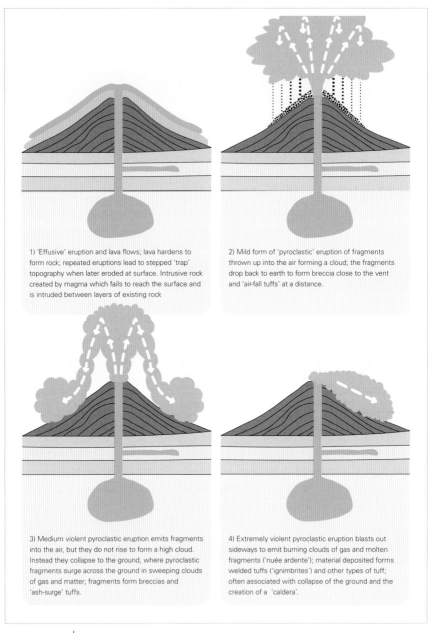

1) 'Effusive' eruption and lava flows; lava hardens to form rock; repeated eruptions lead to stepped 'trap' topography when later eroded at surface. Intrusive rock created by magma which fails to reach the surface and is intruded between layers of existing rock

2) Mild form of 'pyroclastic' eruption of fragments thrown up into the air forming a cloud; the fragments drop back to earth to form breccia close to the vent and 'air-fall tuffs' at a distance.

3) Medium violent pyroclastic eruption emits fragments into the air, but they do not rise to form a high cloud. Instead they collapse to the ground, where pyroclastic fragments surge across the ground in sweeping clouds of gas and matter; fragments form breccias and 'ash-surge' tuffs.

4) Extremely violent pyroclastic eruption blasts out sideways to emit burning clouds of gas and molten fragments ('nuée ardente'); material deposited forms welded tuffs ('ignimbrites') and other types of tuff; often associated with collapse of the ground and the creation of a 'caldera'.

Diagram 9.2 | Lava, pyroclastic rocks and intrusive rocks.

Granite is a rhyolitic rock that has cooled slowly, deep underground, to produce rock with large crystals. When erupted onto the surface and cooled rapidly, rhyolitic magma produces a type of rock known as 'rhyolitic tuff'. 'Granitic' and 'rhyolitic' are thus synonyms (these names are categorised in Diagram 8.1). We are entering tough terrain here, with complex and ever-changing terminology. By one assessment there are over 1,500 different classifications of igneous rocks and, as with metamorphic rocks, you can download the latest igneous rock-naming standards from the British Geological Survey website. I will minimise the number of terms and concepts, but it is useful to learn a few of the key names as the nature of the magma affects the type of eruption, rock, scenery and weathering patterns as well as the types of lichen and vegetation.

An idea of how caldera creating eruptions take place can be gained from an explosion in 1912 at Novarupta, near Mount Katmai in Alaska. Before the eruption Katmai was itself a cone volcano, but it was 'beheaded' when it was ripped apart in the sizeable 'ignimbrite' or 'ash-flow' Novarupta eruption. The whole eruptive activity lasted for about 60 hours, with three phases each separated by a few hours and consisting of several individual explosive eruptions of incandescent magma and bits of the surrounding mountains, such as Mount Katmai. The eruptions were accompanied by 14 earthquakes over magnitude 6.0. Incredibly, the eruptions took place 10km from the point where the caldera collapse occurred. The caldera was above the magma chamber, but as it left the chamber, instead of going straight up, the magma found a way sideways and upwards through rock strata to the point of eruption.

Caldera eruptions often involve different phases; the earlier phases result from basaltic or andesitic magma, thus producing lava, and the later phases result from rhyolitic/granitic magma so producing very violent, caldera-creating, fragmental (pyroclastic) explosions (see Diagram 9.2). Whether this is because different magma types separate out as they melt at different temperatures, or whether different pulses of magma from different sources enter the magma chamber in succession, is not really known. (No-one has ever gone down into a magma chamber for a look, meaning that we have to rely on seismic analysis and evolving magma theory to outline the possibilities.)

Having established some of the basic science behind the different types of volcanic eruption, we can look at what is now known about the volcanoes that produced Glen Coe's magnificent mountains during the subduction and continental collision of the Caledonian mountain-building episode. The eruptions of the present-day Glen Coe area all took place over a period of about 2–3 million years in a series of phases. The first phase was probably the eruption of masses of lava, but there is no direct evidence of this lava as it has all been eroded away.

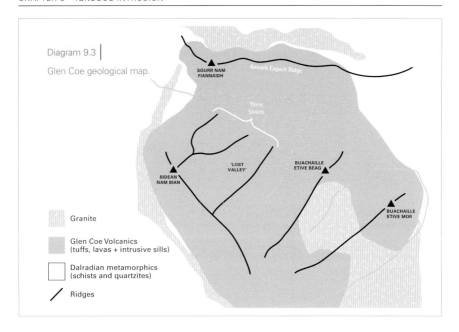

Diagram 9.3

Glen Coe geological map.

SGURR NAM
FIANNAIDH

Aonach Eagach Ridge

Three
Sisters

'LOST
VALLEY'

BUACHAILLE
ETIVE BEAG

BIDEAN
NAM BIAN

BUACHAILLE
ETIVE MOR

Granite

Glen Coe Volcanics
(tuffs, lavas + intrusive sills)

Dalradian metamorphics
(schists and quartzites)

Ridges

The Glen Coe area is very rich in sheet-like 'sills' of basaltic and andesitic magma that did not quite reach the surface, having been injected into partly solidified surrounding rock. As the later overlying rock was removed by millions of years of erosion, these sills are now exposed at the surface in some places. The 'Basal Andesitic Sill Complex' forms a very prominent feature in Glen Coe, making up the lower part of the immensely impressive rock bastion known as Aonach Dubh (the westernmost of the Three Sisters). It is up to 500m thick in places, with individual sills between 20 and 30m thick, and is concentrated in the north and west of the area.

The boundary between the sill complex and the overlying tuffs is best seen on the west flank of Aonach Dubh from down valley, for example, from near the National Park visitor centre. The boundary can also be distinguished from the main lay-by opposite the Three Sisters, or from the north Glen Coe ridge (see Photo 9.3 and Diagram 9.4).

There followed the seven massive pyroclastic eruptions (each 'eruption' consisting of a series of closely related eruptions) combined with 'volcanotectonic' faulting. In other words, there was much dropping down of different areas with the movement taking place along the lines of faults within the developing caldera as the land collapsed down into the increasingly voided magma chamber.

Photo 9.3 + Diagram 9.4 | The Three Sisters of Glen Coe.

Viewed from roadside lay-by in Glen Coe.

As mentioned above, the eruptions were the hottest and most violent type of pyroclastic explosion where the rhyolitic magma bursts out in a sideways flow as a mass of incandescent gas, magma, 'pumice' (essentially volcanic 'froth') and torn-away lumps of the existing rock. This cloud rushed forwards at speeds of hundreds of kilometres per hour at an incredible temperature (between 700 and 900°C) in what geologists call a 'nuée ardente'; literally, a burning cloud. More prosaically, it is also known as an 'ash flow', 'pyroclastic flow', and sometimes an 'ignimbrite' eruption. All these terms are used in different ways by different writers. I will keep it simple and refer to 'ash-flow' eruptions.

The rocks formed from hardened fragments of magma ('ash') are known as 'tuffs'. With the ash-flow type of eruption, we end up with 'ash-flow tuffs'. One common subtype of 'ash-flow tuff' is known as a 'welded tuff', formed when the fragments of magma, melted lumps of pumice and pre-existing rock are all welded into the fabric of the ash when the burning cloud settles and cools. Welded tuffs are often quite distinctive with flattened lumps of pumice and pre-existing rock forming easily identifiable streaks (see Photo w16.1). These rocks are common in the Glen Coe area.

Not all ash-flow material cools to form welded tuffs, however, and there are many varieties of rock that result from ash-flow eruptions. Sometimes the incredibly hot ash-flow cloud acts almost like a liquid and the same type of flow-banding observed in solidified lavas can also be seen in ash-flow tuffs. This is also a common feature in and around Glen Coe. It is worth pointing out that geologists did indeed originally classify such rocks as lava or 'lava-like'; it is only in recent years that ash-flow eruptions have been better understood. Although the eruption is fragmental the incandescent cloud of matter sometimes takes on the characteristics of a liquid flow, leaving features such as a very fine flow-banding (see Photo 9.4). Pyroclastic rocks can also be brecciated similar to lava (see Photo 9.5), in which case the rock is properly known as breccia. The lumps are fragments of solidified magma and bits of the existing rocks ripped apart in the explosion. The larger the lumps found, the closer the location to the vent where the eruption took place.

Geologists now believe that there were seven different episodes of ash-flow type eruptions, each deepening and expanding the caldera. They reckon that as much as 700m of 'downthrow' occurred on some of the major faults within the caldera. Much of the erupted material would have fallen outside the caldera, but obviously a lot ponded within the expanding caldera depression. This ponded material is what we see today forming the mountains on either side of Glen Coe; the 'outflow' material that escaped the caldera has all been eroded away.

Photo 9.4 | Flow-banding in rhyolitic tuff.

Photo 9.5 | Brecciated rhyolitic tuff (volcanic breccia).

The ring-fault which curves round the western, northern and eastern borders of the area used to be seen as a single coherent structure along which the whole caldera plunged down, piston-like, in a mega-eruption. Geologists now believe that it was created piecemeal and represents a series of massive eruptions. Another massive blob of rhyolitic magma was created underground following these eruptions, but instead of rising all the way to the surface it slowly solidified underground forming a granite pluton. This is now known as the Clach Leathad pluton, which stretches south from the south-eastern edge of the caldera (on the south-eastern flanks of Buachaille Etive Mor).

Despite the difficulty of creating detailed mapping on the very steep slopes of the Glen Coe mountains, geologists have now produced some very fine analyses of the different ash-flow eruptions. A coherent account of the different phases and rock types produced – of which there is a great variety – has been provided, and it is possible for the hillwalker to distinguish some of the key rock types. The great crags cutting into the mountains on the southern side of the glen have produced cross-sections through which geologists have studied the creation of the Glen Coe caldera, and the observant hillwalker can pick out many of the key features in these slopes.

It is fairly straightforward to distinguish the underlying andesitic lavas from the overlying rhyolitic tuffs on Aonach Dubh, the westernmost of the Three Sisters. This is especially the case from lower down Glen Coe, from down in Glen Coe itself (such as from the big lay-by opposite Coire Gabhair – 'the Lost Valley') or from the northern side of Glen Coe either on the Aonach Eagach ridge (for climbers and serious scramblers) or from between Sron Gharbh and Stob Mhic Mhartuin (accessed from the Devil's Staircase on the West Highland Way for walkers).

Photo 9.6
Buachaille
Etive Mor.

It is less easy for the hillwalker to identify all the various types of rhyolitic and andesitic tuffs found in great variety on the Three Sisters and the two Buachaille Etives. It is not difficult however to notice when you have crossed from one rock type to another walking along the ridges of either Buachaille Etive Mor (see Photo 9.6) or Buachaille Etive Beag. Geologists have assigned various names to these different rocks with labels such as the Upper Streaky Andesites (wittily yielding the abbreviation USA), the Three Sisters Ignimbrite Member, the Lower Etive Rhyolite or the Upper Queen's Cairn Breccias. In all, there are 23 such different rock 'formations' in the most recent mapping of the Glen Coe caldera area.

Another feature that is easy to spot is the presence of scores of dykes (intruded igneous sheets) that are now exposed on the surface, often appearing as more or less narrow reddish lines running across the slopes and hill tops (see Photos 7.6, w16.3 and w16.4). Once you have spotted one of these dykes you will see them all over the place. Most of the dykes are linear features that run from a few hundred metres to up to 10km in a southwest–northeast alignment across the Glen Coe caldera area, forming a dense swarm. They can be anything from a couple of metres to 10–20m wide. These dykes frequently form 'geomorphological' structures such as cols and gullies. Where this happens it is because of a slight difference in the resistance to erosion between the dyke and the surrounding rock.

One of the key structural constants of the Glen Coe caldera area (persisting from the time of volcanic eruptions up to this very day) is the general drainage pattern which dips roughly from east to west. This general tilt of the land is an underlying tectonic feature, but it cuts across the main direction of a large swarm of intrusive 'dykes'. These dykes can often have an influence on scenery on a small scale.

The main shaping agent of the volcanic rocks in the area has been frozen water in the form of glaciers carving out deep valleys along lines of weakness. As these are often faults which have also been exploited by magma to create dykes and sills, the valleys of Glen Coe reflect the underlying geological history. Bealach Dearg, the col at the head of Coire Gabhail, is centred on a dyke which provided a weakness on which the ice could work. There is not always such a direct relation however, and plenty of dykes cross the landscape without creating an obvious landscape feature. The beauty of the relationship between geology and scenery is that it requires a modest degree of effort and thought to work it all out. Glen Coe is certainly one of the most rewarding places in the Highlands for expending that effort and thought.

CHAPTER 10

Atlantic Appearance

We have looked at the rocks and the geological structure of the Northern and Grampian Highlands in the previous five chapters, relating most of this to the great collision of continental plates that took place during the destruction of the Iapetus oceanic plate and the formation of the supercontinent Pangea.

When the collision of the continents started to take place, the ancient rocks of present-day Scotland and northern Ireland formed several 'terranes' located on or near the edge of the continent Laurentia. These terranes or chunks of continental plate were located near to one another, but not joined in their present-day pattern. The Northern Highlands Terrane (the Moine rocks) was located further to the northeast than the other terranes, opposite the present-day Scandinavian Terrane.

The collision brought Laurentia into collision with Avalonia. It was home to the rocks that today form southern Britain (roughly England and Wales) and southern Ireland. The oldest rocks found there are 'only' about 700 million years old (on Anglesey). From that time, sedimentary and volcanic rocks were created that today crop out as the Lake District of England and Snowdonia in Wales. This happened as the ocean between Laurentia and Avalonia was slowly being subducted out of existence. When the ocean had been fully destroyed, Avalonia was propelled into direct contact with that part of Laurentia where Scotland and northern Ireland were to be found.

In previous chapters, we have looked in some detail at the metamorphosis, igneous activity, deformation and thrusting generated by this collision. One further aspect of this mega-mash-up is significant: the 'suturing' of southern Britain and southern Ireland with Scotland and northern Ireland, which also occurred when Laurentia and Avalonia collided. It was a very effective welding job; the suture which runs roughly along the boundary between Scotland and England was to prove extremely resistant to geological separation a few millions of years later.

When the restless convection currents deep within the earth eventually started to diverge, the Pangean supercontinent was ripped apart. Laurentia tore free to form north

America. A new ocean, the Atlantic, appeared between Avalonia and Laurentia. Avalonia remained grouped with Baltica and Iberia forming western Europe, but the rift did not take place entirely or very neatly along the old boundary between the continents.

Scotland and northern Ireland were ripped away from Laurentia and attached to southern Britain and southern Ireland, so forming the geological structure of the present-day British and Irish Isles. The transaction was not all one-way; Greenland left Europe to become part of the north American plate. It's a bit like removing an excessively sticky label from a book cover, some bits of the label remain while bits of the cover get torn away.

The 'rifting' of the continent and the opening up of the present-day Atlantic Ocean brought considerable volcanic activity. The vast eruptions created the rocks of many of the present-day Scottish Isles (including Mull, Skye, Rum, Canna, Eigg, Muck and Arran). The eruptions also created the rocks of a small chunk of the mainland, the Ardnamurchan peninsula.

Photo 10.1 | Rum (left) and Eigg (right) from Ardnamurchan, volcanic landscape created some 60 million years ago during the initial opening of the Atlantic Ocean.

Although a superficial glance at a map of Scotland gives the impression that Ardnamurchan is an island, it is in fact the most westerly point of the British mainland. Lying directly north of Mull, it is indeed easily associated with the islands rather than the mainland. Of course, it is simply the present-day sea level which determines what is island and what is mainland, so the division is anyway rather arbitrary.

However, as Ardnamurchan is today part of the mainland, it comes within the scope of this book. This is fortunate as it is an enchanting place to visit for its wild scenery and unique geological feature – concentric rings of igneous hills. Its hills are fairly low (reaching up to about

450m above sea level) compared with the bigger mountains of the Highlands, yet they are remote places offering walking as tough (and as rewarding) as any other part of the mainland (see Walks 14 and 15). To discover the geological history of Ardnamurchan we need to go back in time to around 65 million years ago to the birth of the Atlantic as the plates pulled apart.

The present theory is that the 'rifting' or pulling apart of the continental plate was prompted by the fairly sudden (in geological terms) emergence of a very hot 'mantle plume' rising directly from the edge of the earth's core. To reach the outer mantle it created a diverging convection current capable of stretching and breaking open the continental plate, causing volcanic eruptions.

When a continental plate is stretched by the earth's inner convection currents it starts to 'rift', that is, to thin and crack, pulling apart along linear fault zones. As the plate becomes thinner, the underlying mantle gets closer to the surface and pressure is reduced, lowering the melting point of the mantle rocks. If the stretching continues for long enough, molten magma will eventually break through at the surface creating new oceanic plate.

This process of creating the Atlantic Ocean started about 65 million years ago. For the next 10 million years, eruptions poured out enormous quantities of lava which left some very special island landscapes such as the amazing 'columnar jointing' of Fingal's Cave on Staffa (and Giant's Causeway on mainland Northern Ireland). What geologists refer to as 'trap topography' was produced on Skye, Mull and Eigg. 'Trap' is German for 'step' and describes the way sheets of lava stack on top of one another – erosion eats into the rock at rock boundaries, creating ledges between sheets and forming the steps.

The first eruptions which created some of the rocks of present-day Ardnamurchan took place 61 million years ago on the island of Mull. This lava flowed at least as far as some of present-day Ardnamurchan, and is found today to the east of Ben Hiant where it forms a hummocky trap topography (see Photo 10.2).

Photo 10.2 | Lava from the Mull eruptions flowed some way to the north and forms the hummocky 'trap topography' to the east of Ben Hiant, Ardnamurchan.

This massive lava flow was followed by the intrusion (and also eruption) of magma directly below present-day Ardnamurchan, the first of three such magma injections. The magma formed what geologists call 'central-type volcanoes' or 'central complex' volcanoes. The magma is thought to rise up a central plug or conduit, but splays outwards in curved sheets from a focal point some distance underground to form a cone-shaped subterranean structure. The curved sheets certainly appear to form concentric rings, but it is not clear whether a ring is created by several linked sheets or in a continuous form. Some geologists suggest that the rings represent collapsed central plugs, rather than dykes seeking a way to the surface. Present-day central complex volcanoes found elsewhere in the world rise up to heights of 3–4km and are about 50–75km in diameter on the surface; such volcanoes pump out vast volumes of magma.

What we see today on Ardnamurchan are the highly eroded underground remains of the conical sheets, forming distinctly ring-shaped and concentric sets of hills. The present-day outcrops are no more than 5–10km in diameter, so we are seeing the cone shapes just a short distance above the point where the single plug breaks out into conical sheets, which was well below the surface at the time of eruption. The view of the ring of hills is most evident from a viewpoint such as Meall Meadhoin, near the highest point on the most impressive ring (see Walk 15).

Most of the hills we see today date from a third central complex volcano eruption about 59 million years ago. This is because the second central complex volcano largely destroyed evidence of the first, and the third then destroyed much of the evidence of the second. However, the summit of Ben Hiant is the product of the first central complex volcano, known prosaically as 'Centre 1'. The rocks comprising the summit area are from an intrusion, formed by rocks which did not erupt but cooled down on their way. Another outcrop of 'Centre 1' is found on the eastern flank of the complex of rings north of Ben Hiant. Surprisingly, there also remains a very small outcrop of 'Centre 1' right in the middle of the most substantial ring of 'Centre 3' hills (reached on Walk 15).

'Centre 2' created the set of hills forming a partial ring in the south-western corner of the peninsula including the most easily accessible point for an overview of the rings: Beinn na Seilg. The hills in this small area form only an arc, much of the rest having been either destroyed by the later 'Centre 3' eruption and by erosion.

'Centre 3' forms the most impressive of the Ardnamurchan ring complex, consisting of several complete concentric rings of intrusive igneous rock. The rocks forming the 'Centre 3' rings are mainly of a type known as 'gabbro' (see Photo 10.3). This is a rock well known to walkers and climbers on the Isle of Skye as it is common on the popular Cuillin ridge; otherwise, gabbro is rare on the Scottish mainland. Gabbro is formed of large crystals from slow-cooling magma at a depth of 2–3km below the earth's crust (although the magma was originally created at a depth of 60–110km towards the base of the continental plate).

Photo 10.3 | Gabbro: a large-grained basaltic intrusive igneous rock forming the rings of hills in Ardnamurchan.

If the magma had cooled slightly quicker, it would have formed the medium-grained rock known as 'dolerite'; much faster cooling would have led to the formation of the very fine-grained rock known as 'basalt' (see Diagram 8.1). Any magma that did make its way to the surface of these central complex volcanoes would have flowed as basaltic lava. There are no remains of any such lava and, if any did once exist, it has been entirely eroded away. All we are left with is some of the gabbro formed deep down below the surface.

The finest ring, which includes the highest point in the complex Meall nan Con (Walk 15), is made of a type of gabbro known as 'eucrite'. This most impressive feature is therefore known to geologists as the 'Great Eucrite'. The ring of hills has been deeply eroded and offers fine but tough walking with lots of ups and downs. Aerial photographs (and geology maps) show the rings in great clarity. As this book is for hillwalkers, it is pleasing to say that they are also distinguishable on the ground both from Ben Hiant (see Photo w14.2) and from within the ring complex itself (see Photo w15.2).

Another feature of the igneous activity around this time was the creation of a 'dyke swarm'. This is probably the single most conspicuous feature on geology maps of Scotland as a whole. It is marked as a mass of lines, often in stark red (but coloured green on the latest British Geology Survey map of the 'Bedrock Geology' of 'UK North'). The lines appear on all the islands between Skye and Arran and also on the mainland. They are often quite short and only a few kilometres in length, but in southeast and southern Scotland there are some dyke swarms of much longer lengths (e.g. up to tens of kilometres). Ranging in width from about 1m to 1km, the majority are under 10m wide. They are most dense around the areas of the central complex volcanoes that formed the islands and Ardnamurchan. An example of one of the dykes running across the lower flanks of Ben Hiant is seen in Photo w14.2. The dykes are mainly aligned northwest to southeast, and probably represent the lines of fault zones of the original rifting of the continental crust where molten magma rose up.

The series of central complex volcanoes which created Ardnamurchan and several of Scotland's islands has been described as a failed attempt to open up an Atlantic Ocean. Although there was rifting and subsequent eruptions onto the surface, the rifting did not continue to pull apart the continental plate at this point. Instead, the ocean actually appeared somewhat further west, creating the rift that is still active today volcanically and tectonically and is known as the Mid-Atlantic Ridge. The mid-oceanic ridge is where the ocean floor is being created by ceaseless volcanic eruption, pushing into the existing ocean crust (part of the process of 'ocean floor spreading'). The Mid-Atlantic Ridge actually rises up above sea level where Iceland is now found, perhaps because a powerful convection current (in the form of a 'mantle plume') rises up from very deep below this point.

Volcanoes have been active in Iceland and on the Mid-Atlantic Ridge ever since the eruptions that created Ardnamurchan, Skye and Mull. They create a direct link between the process that created rocks some 60 million years ago and the continued tectonic activity of this region of the globe, that is, the slow but sure spreading of the Atlantic Ocean. Some day the inner convection currents will change. It is likely then that the continents will once again be driven towards each other to form a supercontinent as the earth's great tectonic cycle continues.

In the meantime, we exist in an 'inter-glacial' period (not withstanding the effects of human-induced climate change). In the next chapter we will look at the way in which glaciation affected the scenery of the Highlands. We can note here that Ardnamurchan was fully covered by glaciers when the last ice age was at its most intense. Very considerable amounts of rock have been eroded away to create the landscape of today, exposing the inner workings of the 60 million year old ring-shaped central complex of volcanoes in a most remarkable way.

Photo 10.4 | Ben Hiant seen from Clach Chiarain. A quartz-diorite intrusion from the 'Centre 1' ring complex eruption forms the top of Ben Hiant, with lava visible from centre left across the photo.

CHAPTER 11

Glacial Gouging

We have seen in previous chapters how the rocks of the present-day Scottish Highlands were formed by seemingly endless eons of sedimentation, intense bursts of volcanic activity and slow relentless application of forces sufficient to result in metamorphosis, deformation and mountain building. These forces were the product of massive tectonic events such as the collision of continents and subduction of oceanic plates. With some geological knowledge, we can find more or less indirect evidence of these great forces. However, what we see out on the hills of Scotland is primarily a glacial landscape. The tough igneous and metamorphic rocks offered a highly resistant landscape which powerful glaciers ripped into, cutting deep valleys and sharp ridges and leaving atmospheric corries, enchanting lochans and elongated lochs.

Ice is the fastest-acting agent of erosion. Before considering the role of ice in fashioning the landforms of the Highlands however, it is worth noting some other forces which wear away and shape the landscape. We can divide erosion into two categories: chemical and physical.

Chemical weathering takes place as soon as a rock surface is exposed to the atmosphere. The rate of chemical erosion depends very much on the rock type and whether the minerals of which it comprises are chemically stable or reactive. Rocks high in silica (such as most sandstone, quartzite and rhyolitic igneous rocks) are generally less chemically active, while rocks derived from basaltic minerals (such as lavas and clays) are more susceptible to chemical activity.

One problem facing the hillwalker when it comes to distinguishing rock types is that all rocks look more or less grey. Geologists hammer away a sample and take it back to the laboratory to study it in various ways, allowing them to apply labels such as 'rhyolitic tuff' or 'metamorphic schist'. They are interested in the inner rock, before it starts to weather and change its chemical structure. As hillwalkers we are confined to distinguishing rocks from the weathered surface using features such as slight variations in colour (reddish Torridonian sandstone and pink Cairngorms granite), linear features (welded tuffs and gneiss) and shine (of schist and quartzite) as diagnostic aids.

Sometimes you will come across a rock which has recently been broken. Such rocks will typically show a surface colour (the weathered face) which is different to the internal colour (the fresh face). This illustrates the change that rocks undergo as they weather chemically (see Photos 11.1 and 2.7). It is not always a straightforward colour change, however, as the chemical weathering may occur in stages. For example, it is quite common for a freshly exposed face to be (say) blueish in colour, for recently exposed faces to be reddish or brownish and for long exposed faces to be greyish.

Photo 11.1 | A broken rock (andesitic igneous rock from Ben Nevis) shows the dark grey (and white flecked) fresh face in the centre and left; contrasted with the weathered faces (whitish) seen on the right.

One further complication is that lichen (a symbiosis of fungus and algae) grows on rock surfaces, speeding up chemical weathering and adding more colour variations to be taken into account. It is generally true to say that chemically inert rocks, such as high-silica rocks, support less-abundant lichen growth (and thus less variation in colour) than chemically reactive rocks (such as the clay-producing basalts).

The rate of chemical weathering is usually fairly slow, but not inappreciable. Some idea of the rate of rock surface removal can be gauged from the way in which glacial 'striations' (scratches left on rock surfaces by rock fragments embedded in a passing glacier flow) are only visible in newly exposed rocks (see Photo w16.6). Such recent exposures can often be found alongside footpaths, where passing boots have removed vegetation cover from a bit of rock adjacent to the track. Once a rock has been exposed to the air for some time, enough of the rock surface will have been weathered away to below the depth of the striations.

Physical erosion can work at a much faster timescale than chemical weathering. We can divide the forces of physical erosion into two: wind and water. The role of wind, most especially in dry regions, is often underestimated. Chemical erosion can often break up the cement holding the individual grains of sand in exposed sandstone, thus 'liberating' the grains. The wind then whips up the sand grains and literally sandblasts rocks into finer shapes.

The power of running water is best seen in gorges and waterfalls. A typical waterfall is found at a boundary between two rock types which have quite different resistance. For example, if underlying layers of a rock are quite weak a waterfall can develop when the water begins to remove the lower layers, eventually causing the upper layers to be undermined and thus to collapse. If the stream is already running along the line of a fault, then the waterfall can fairly easily cut back to form a gorge (see Photo 11.2).

Photo 11.2 | Gorge cut into quartzite, Assynt.

Even if you have seen mountain streams and rivers in full spate, the presence of a tiny stream running in a great gorge may make it difficult to imagine the forces which created such a gash in the rock. The explanation is that the gorge was probably created by glacial meltwaters, incredibly powerful flows of water that can carve astonishing features in the landscape.

Most hillwalkers will have seen rivers and burns in flood flow. Many will have experienced being turned back by impassable water courses transformed from quiet little burns. The water in such flows is brown with sediment being carried away to be dumped lower down to form mud, silt and sand (and later to become mudstone, siltstone and sandstone). Unseen beneath the churning flow are the larger pebbles and rocks which the water push and bump along the stream or river bed, chipping minute amounts off the underlying rock.

A characteristic feature of water and stone at work are the holes seen carved into rock by confined waters. A good place to see this is in Glen Nevis (see Walk 13) at the narrowest point of the gorge, just before the valley opens out with a view of the An Steall waterfall. At this point the track is just above the stream (which is largely hidden by a mass of collapsed boulders) and large holes can be seen where eddy currents have caused loose stones and small boulders to carve into the rock (see photo w13.3). If you look upwards, following the upper crag sides, you can see many such holes rising all the way up. The higher the holes, the less sharp their outline due to chemical weathering of the rock surface. You can however see how the river has (step by step) cut down into the rock when carrying large amounts of debris-laden glacial meltwater. Each group of holes represents a previous riverbed in this remarkable scene.

However impressive the power of running water, it is ice and the combination of liquid water and solid ice which have had the most dramatic effect on the scenery of the Highlands. Notwithstanding the consequences of human-induced global climate change, we are currently in an inter-glacial period. The present glacial episode began about 2.5 million years ago. There have been repeated periods of widespread glaciation since then, interspersed with inter-glacial periods where glaciers are restricted to the polar regions and high mountainous ranges. The last cold period only came to an end about 11,000 years ago (with a short cold blip around 9,500 years ago).

The key to the development of glacier ice is the temperature during the summer. If winter snows do not melt over summer, then snow will start to accumulate in thicker layers. When this happens, the lower layers of snow are compressed and air is expelled. The snow is slowly transformed from snow into 'firn' ice and then into 'blue' or 'glacier' ice. If the ice covers a substantial area, it can form an 'ice sheet' (see Diagram 11.1). If it is confined to a valley it forms an 'outlet glacier' (from an ice sheet) or a 'valley glacier' (see Photo 11.3). A small glacier may be limited to a small area on the side of a mountain, known as a 'corrie glacier' (see Photo 11.4).

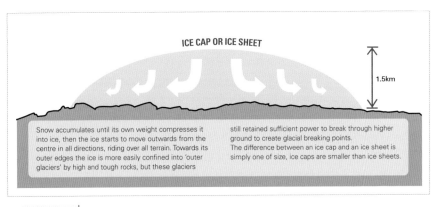

ICE CAP OR ICE SHEET

1.5km

Snow accumulates until its own weight compresses it into ice, then the ice starts to move outwards from the centre in all directions, riding over all terrain. Towards its outer edges the ice is more easily confined into 'outer glaciers' by high and tough rocks, but these glaciers still retained sufficient power to break through higher ground to create glacial breaking points.
The difference between an ice cap and an ice sheet is simply one of size, ice caps are smaller than ice sheets.

Diagram 11.1 | Ice caps and ice sheets.

Photo 11.3 | Valley glacier, Himalayas. Photo: Ian Smith.

Photo 11.4 | Corrie glacier, Vanoise, French Alps. The moraines at the base of the glacier show the extent of glacier melting over recent decades; the photo also depicts intense deformation folding ('nappe') raised from a deep thrust zone on the right-hand face of the peak (Grande Casse).

So much weight accumulates that the lowest part of the glacier ice eventually starts to deform and move outwards – a glacier can reasonably be described as a river of ice. Plastic and brittle deformation are involved in the movement of the ice. The glacier will rip apart the scenery as it flows, digging down into the rock to create gorges, deep valleys, corries and other glacial features. An important aspect of the way ice flows is that its effects vary considerably. One area may suffer immense erosion, while another adjacent area is hardly touched. This applies especially to large bodies of ice, such as ice sheets. The Cairngorms illustrate this quite well with gently rolling hills apparently unaffected by ice, separated only by a few deep glacial valleys and corries.

The ice age involved a series of colder and warmer periods. There were times when the climate was particularly cold and when an ice sheet would have covered everything but the tops of the highest mountains. This means that ice has shaped even the highest parts of the Highlands. Glacial 'scouring' of higher parts is quite common, leaving complex areas of intensely hummocky terrain, often with small lochs or boggy areas, with an overall flattish or gently sloping aspect. The 'knocks' or small humps appear to be quite random when you are within their realm, and often present tough navigational challenges. Seen from a high viewpoint, however, they often form a pattern that reflects lines of weakness in the rocks such as faults and rock boundaries.

Breabag (Walk 4) is a good example. Its basic structure reflects great thrusts of quartzite that have been piled up on top of one another, quite evident from near the summit area (see Photo w4.10). While ascending from the bealach (col), each knock looks like it must be the summit as it hides a view of the higher knocks. The same effect is seen at a very large scale at lower heights in the large area of exposed ancient gneiss in the northwest of the Highlands (the classic area of 'knock and lochan' topography). There are fewer high points here and the 'grain' of the landscape is difficult to discern, unless from the summit of a neighbouring mountain such as Ben Stack (see Photo w2.3) or Quinag (Walk 3).

Ice would have found its way outwards from the centre of the ice sheet using 'outlet' glaciers. In some cases the outlet glaciers found an easy route, following existing river valleys. In other cases however it was necessary for the ice to smash through the watershed that lies near the western side of the Highlands, creating glacial 'breaching points' or 'breaches'.

The line of the present-day watershed is probably much the same as the pre-glacial version, but it has been lowered considerably in dozens of places by glacial breaching (see Photo 11.5). At least some of the ice flowing out from the centre of the ice sheet (located to the east of the watershed) would have flowed west, even though this involved some uphill movement: so great is the pressure created by accumulated ice. All the same, the ice would have followed the easiest route, becoming concentrated on pre-existing low points on the watershed. Being confined, the ice would have had greater cutting power and the existing low points were carved into breaches, anything up to 700m lower than before the ice age.

Photo 11.5 | Glacial breaching point where ice from valley glaciers crossed mountain flanks, Lochan Meall an t- Suidhe, Ben Nevis.

In the case of the Great Glen, the combined effect of cutting out an outlet valley and glacial breaching has resulted in a great trench which crosses the Highlands from one side to the other. It is of course no coincidence that this valley has been cut along the line of a great fault in the earth's crust. Indeed, several of the large glens of the Highlands are also located on faults or other weaknesses in the rocks (such as boundaries between rock types). These same valleys would have been the site of valley glaciers when the temperature was somewhat less cold and the great ice sheets had melted (see Photo 11.6 and Diagram 11.2).

Photo 11.6 | Loch Maree, cut by a 'valley glacier' along the line of a major fault.

Diagram 11.2 | Glacial valley deepening and deposition of moraines.

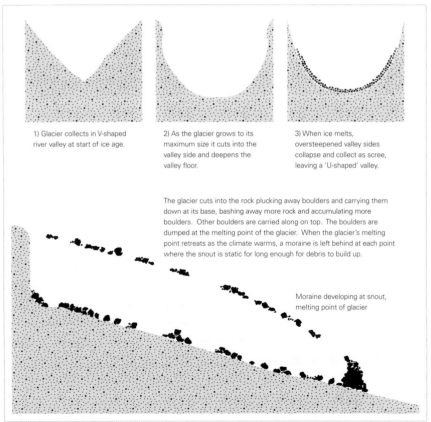

1) Glacier collects in V-shaped river valley at start of ice age.

2) As the glacier grows to its maximum size it cuts into the valley side and deepens the valley floor.

3) When ice melts, oversteepened valley sides collapse and collect as scree, leaving a 'U-shaped' valley.

The glacier cuts into the rock plucking away boulders and carrying them down at its base, bashing away more rock and accumulating more boulders. Other boulders are carried along on top. The boulders are dumped at the melting point of the glacier. When the glacier's melting point retreats as the climate warms, a moraine is left behind at each point where the snout is static for long enough for debris to build up.

Moraine developing at snout, melting point of glacier

The combined effect of the outlet glacier and the valley glacier would have carved deep down into the rock. This happened when sea level was much lower than today (because of the quantity of seawater locked up in snowfields and glaciers), so the glaciers cut down lower into the rock than present-day sea level. This is reflected in a key aspect of the Highlands scenery: the long narrow freshwater and marine lochs that bring such extraordinary beauty into the landscape.

The freshwater lochs mainly owe their existence to the way glaciers cut more deeply when they are confined, for example between a run of much more resistant rock. Here the ice will cut down, carving out a classic 'U-shaped' valley. At either end of the resistant rock, the ice will have cut a shallower and wider valley. This means that the valley floor becomes deeper or shallower (depending on the rock type) over its length, creating 'rock basins'. If the rock basin becomes shallow enough to reach and remain above sea level, then a freshwater loch will collect. Otherwise, the valley becomes one of the long marine inlet lochs often called 'sea lochs' or 'fjords'.

Loch Morar is the deepest freshwater loch at just over 300m deep. Loch Ness is second deepest and second largest in terms of surface area, but far and away the largest in terms of volume of water. Loch Lomond has the largest surface area, but is fairly shallow at its southern end. Indeed, it becomes so wide and shallow that there are quite a few islands which break the surface at the southern end, including the line of islands which mark the Highland Boundary fault (see Photos 1.1 and w18.4). At its northern end however, where it is narrow and confined between tough rock, Loch Lomond is much deeper.

Loch Maree also demonstrates how geology determines the depth of a rock basin. It is deepest where it is squeezed between the resistant rocks of Slioch and Meall a' Ghuibhas. It used to be thought that rock basins generally get deeper towards the end from which they drain, suddenly getting shallower at the very end, but this view is now disregarded. About one-third of rock basin lochs are deepest at their drainage end, one third in the middle part and one third in the upper part.

The great glens and lochs of the Highlands are a scenic attraction. The great outlet-glacier and major breaching-point valleys are often the only feasible places for roads and railways, so they offer all visitors their first glimpse of the Highlands. Indeed, for the majority of visitors, the view from the valley is what they see of the mountain landscape. Glacial work is not however confined to carving valleys and rock basins – there are also many glacial features that do not sport roads and which require you to don boots and walk into them to discover their secrets.

Perhaps the most cherished of glacial features is the corrie (see Diagram 11.3). A corrie is classically an amphitheatre-shaped carving into the hillside, encasing a lochan behind a 'rockbar' (see Photo 11.7). Once again, geology is usually the deciding factor in the shape of a corrie.

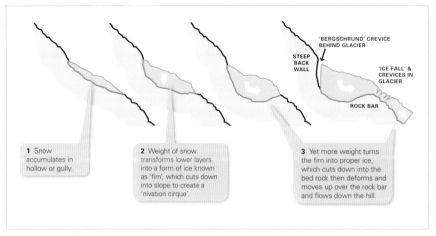

'BERGSCHRUND' CREVICE
BEHIND GLACIER

STEEP
BACK
WALL

'ICE-FALL' &
CREVICES IN
GLACIER

ROCK BAR

1 Snow accumulates in hollow or gully.

2 Weight of snow transforms lower layers into a form of ice known as 'firn', which cuts down into slope to create a 'nivation cirque'.

3 Yet more weight turns the firn into proper ice, which cuts down into the bed rock then deforms and moves up over the rock bar and flows down the hill.

Diagram 11.3 | Formation of corrie glaciers.

Photo 11.7 | Glacial corrie, Meall Coire Choille-rais.

Corries form in clumps, usually facing north–northeast where there is least sunlight and where the prevailing south-westerly winds blow vast quantities of snow which then collects in hollows sheltered from the wind. This effect is seen in many places, for example Beinn Eighe (Walk 6), Beinn Bhan (Walk 7), Craig Meagaidh (Walk 10) and Glencoe (Walk 16). Beinn Bhàn exemplifies the common landscape of a smooth grassy slope on the western side, running up to an extremely sharp edge overlooking near-vertical crags forming the backwalls and sidewalls of these corries. Glencoe shows the same effect on a different relief – here the corries are aligned on the north-facing side of a valley, forming the great chasms cut into the Three Sisters of Glencoe opposite a fairly uneventful hillside on the south-facing slope.

As the snow collects it is compressed, becoming heavier and heavier under its own accumulating weight, and is transformed into ice. Eventually the lowest ice is deformed and begins rotational movement in trying to escape the overlying weight. This cuts down into the hillside, but also leads to upwards motion of the ice until it crosses the lip of the hollow and can flow downwards. Continued rotational movement cuts the corrie deeper and deeper and also cuts back into the rock, forming the amphitheatre shape (see Photos 11.8 and 11.9). The backwall of a corrie is often aligned with jointing planes in the rock which provide weaknesses as they become exposed.

Photo 11.8 |
Glacier corries
in the Alps.

Photo 11.9 |
Ice-free corries
on Liathach.

The corrie can be anything from 300m to more than 1km across and up to a few hundred metres deep. The height at which corries develop is lower in the west (where there is more snowfall) and higher towards the east (where snow lingers for longer).

Some of the corries in the Cairngorms are pretty circular because they have cut down into a uniform rock type. The corries of the Torridonian sandstone on the northwest terrane are clearly shaped by the layered nature of the sandstone; they look like human structures from some angles and can often display considerable circularity in shape. Many of the corries in the northwest have their floors in gneiss while the corrie walls are cut into sandstone (gneiss providing a more resistant rock).

The great corrie of Coire Mhic Fhearchair on the north-western end of Beinn Eighe illustrates the asymmetry of a corrie which develops on an area of mixed rock type. The lower half of the corrie is Torridonian sandstone, but its upper part is quartzite. The rock boundary is so clearly evident on the great cliffs as soon as you enter the corrie (Walk 6), sloping from upper right to lower left. The quartzite-capped sandstone forms the great upright buttresses of the crags on the right but the quartzite, while still a very resistant rock, has different forms at different parts of the corrie. Only about one-quarter of Highland corries have a lochan (although a once-existing lochan has dried up in many more); whether a lochan exists or not again depends on the geology.

Where adjacent corrie glaciers or valley glaciers enlarge, cutting back and sideways towards each other, they can create narrow ridges or 'arêtes' (see Photo 11.10). These offer some of the most exciting hillwalking, scrambling and/or climbing in the Highlands. The list of such features is long, including Foinaven, An Teallach, Càrn Mor Dearg, the Five Sisters of Kintail, the Saddle and many others.

Photo 11.10 | Arête cut by adjacent corrie glaciers, Beinn Bhan, Applecross.

A feature often associated with glaciation is the 'moraine'. As ice cuts into a valley or mountainside, rocks are carried away by the moving ice only to be dumped either alongside the glacier or at its 'snout' or melting point. The rocks then form 'lateral' and 'recessional' moraines, respectively. A recessional moraine may be referred to as a 'terminal' moraine if it marks the furthest point reached by a glacier, but otherwise marks where a glacier snout was present for some time during a retreat of the melting point due to warming temperatures. Any resurgence of the ice would wipe away any such recessional moraines (see Photo 11.11).

Photo 11.11

Hummocky, recessional moraines, Driesh.

Rounded hummocky ground formed from moraine-type material (and distinguished from ice-scoured hummocky terrain formed from solid bedrock mentioned above) is glacial in origin, but whether these patterns represent recessional moraine complexes or deposition underneath a glacier is not clear.

Another high-level glacial feature that needs to be mentioned is the 'meltwater channel'. When temperatures rose and glacial ice melted, large quantities of water built up in ice-dammed lakes (e.g. in and around Glen Roy, Walk 11). As water was released by melting glaciers, it formed a massive series of lakes behind a remaining large glacier in the Great Glen. The lakes spread up Glen Spean, Glen Gloy and Glen Roy until the water reached the height of a bealach over which it could flow, so setting a temporary height for the lake.

As the temperature rose the blocking glacier grew smaller and water could escape by another way, again setting a temporary lake level. This process was repeated once more to set a third lake level which endured after the lake had been fully drained away. Each subsequent lower lake level left the mark of the higher level untouched, and the marks are easily visible today (see Photos 11.12 and w11.1–w11.3). The 'parallel roads' of Glen Roy are one of Scotland's prized geological features and easily accessible to anyone visiting the Ben Nevis area. More 'roads' also exist on the lower flanks of the Ben Nevis massif, under Aonach Mor and the Grey Corries, but are largely hidden by afforestation.

Meltwater flows can be considerably more powerful than ordinary rivers and can carry quite large boulders, leading to considerable physical erosion and the cutting out of remarkable features. A popular example of a gorge cut by glacial meltwater is the Corrieshalloch Gorge near Ullapool, where a meltwater stream has carved a deep, steep-sided gash into a

Photo 11.12 | Looking down Glen Roy with the 'parallel roads' visible on the hillsides.

fault. The gorge is just downstream of a glacial breach just west of Loch Glascarnoch reservoir, not far from Ullapool.

Another meltwater feature is the high-level channel, such as the Chalamain Gap (see Photo w9.1) and The Window on Creag Meagaidh (Photo w10.3). These gaps were carved out by rock-laden meltwater streams acting under great pressure, possibly running underneath a glacier. An alternative explanation is that they could be the creation of a sudden release of a large amount of dammed meltwater, again carrying quantities of boulders which would have acted as battering rams.

The transition back and forth between ice and water is at the heart of another very important aspect of physical weathering: 'freeze-thaw' action. Water has many unusual characteristics, one of which is that it begins to expand as it gets close to freezing. Most matter contracts as it becomes colder, but from 4°C water expands slightly and retains that expansion as it becomes solid ice. As water penetrates deep into any tiny crack, such as a joint in an exposed rock surface, this freezing and expanding action can occur repeatedly (for example, every day in a cold but sunny aspect).

The result of this over time is to break rock surfaces into boulders, forming 'boulder fields' or 'block fields'. These are quite common on summits where freeze-thaw action is at its most intense. The upper part of Ben Nevis is covered in such a block field, although it is often obscured from view by snow (see Photos w12.3 and w12.4).

One final point to make about ice is that such an accumulated weight depressed the plastic mantle rocks (see box 'Deformation' in Chapter 7). Since the end of the ice age, the weight has been removed and the mantle is pushing back up, eventually to resume its original shape. This 'isostatic rebound' is still going on today and, for the time being, the amount of material eroded from the mountains each year (about 1mm) is just about the same as they are pushed upwards by isostatic rebound.

This chapter comprises a rather rapid dash through the variety of chemical and physical weathering forces that have shaped the Highlands, looking at the ways in which summits, ridges, corries, valleys and other features have been created. The sea has been mentioned only indirectly, noting that its level changes with the intensity of global glaciation and how that has led to the flooded valleys or fjords that define the geography of northwest Scotland.

As this book is about the geology of the Highlands, it is perhaps acceptable that little attention has been paid to the sea. However, as this book is also about the landscape of the Highlands, that lack of attention is less forgivable. The scenery of much of the Highlands is dramatically affected by the interplay of mountain and sea, of mainland and island, of rocky cliffs and sandy bay. It is the delightful interplay of light and water that provides some of the most memorable scenic wonders of Scotland.

A few words about the coasts of the Highlands are therefore essential. As the weather can often be pretty dire, making mountain walks an unattractive choice, a path along or near the coast can be a useful alternative on wet or gloomy days. Where there are rock outcrops you can see a lot of detail of different types of rock, especially the gneisses and Torridonian sandstones.

You can also see the seawater at work reducing the land to sand and mud, ready to be recycled into sedimentary rocks. As the sea cuts into the rock it forms cliffs and a 'wave-cut platform'. The cliffs are seldom cut back uniformly. Instead, the retreat is uneven so headlands may be created which eventually become fingers sticking out into the sea with waves crashing on either side. This can lead to the inner part of the finger being undercut to form a natural 'arch'. Eventually the arch collapses leaving a 'stack' – some such as the Old Man of Hoy have become famous for their improbable architecture and the challenge they hold out to rock climbers. Naturally the stacks become unstable and are reduced in size, eventually becoming stumps and then just small lumps of rock before disappearing altogether. The various stages of this process are illustrated in Photos 11.13–11.16, taken on different parts of the northern coast to the east of Durness.

The processes of geology are at work all around you as you walk out in the hills. The mountains may look solid and immutable, but they are in fact either in constant growth or constant decay or both at the same time. As long as the earth's internal convection currents continue to drive the tectonic plates around the surface of the globe, then the geological processes that fashion our planet will continue their constant task of creating and recycling the rocks and the landscape. Nowhere in Britain are the ancient and modern forces of plate tectonics and erosion more obvious to the hillwalker than in the Scottish Highlands.

Photo 11.13–6 | Erosion leads from arches via stacks to stumps; northern coast, east of Durness.

Photo 11.17 | Granite dyke intruded into ancient gneiss (foreground) with dipping Torridonian sandstone (background), Sheigra.

About the Walks

The recommended walks are intended to illustrate a wide range of the geological and scenic features discussed in the first half of the book. I have tried to include as much variety as possible, but I cannot lay claim to completeness. The Highlands form such a large area that any choice of just 18 walks to represent its scenic and geological worth must be arbitrary. The weather has often been the deciding factor, as the walks require sufficiently cloud-free conditions to take the photos needed to illustrate them (as anyone who has walked the hills of the Highlands will appreciate). All the same, I hope that the walks offer a reasonably balanced overview of the different geological areas that have came together in repeated episodes of continental collision.

I have tried to select comparatively shorter walks (in Highlands terms). There are no walks described here which expect you to tramp 22 miles and ascend 1,600m, as is not un-common in hillwalking guides. There are however a few longish walks, for example Ben Nevis inevitably demands a very long ascent of some 1,300 metres. Some of the other walks are quite tough, such as Bidean nam Bean (walk 16) and Meall nan Con on Ardnamurchan (walk 15). Those used to the English or Welsh hills will find the scale and roughness of Scottish hills significantly more demanding. A lot of the walks cross rough or steepish terrain, but I have avoided lengthy narrow ridges, steep slopes and scrambling. 'Narrow' and 'steep' are of course a subjective judgment and some may dispute my assertion in regards to very short sections on Arkle (walk 1), Ben Stack (walk 2), Beinn Bhan (walk 7), Bidean nam Bean (walk 16) and Meall nan Tarmachan (walk 17), which some might find vertigo-inducing.

All the walks are easily and directly accessible from roads and parking places and, in many cases, by public transport (www.travelinescotland.com). I have not shied away from using the odd high-level car park, for example in the Cairngorms (walk 9) and Meall nan Tarmachan (walk 17) to minimise the tally of metres to be climbed.

There are a couple of easier, shorter walks such as Glen Nevis (walk 13), Glen Roy (walk 11) and Ben Hiant on Ardnamurchan (walk 14). The Glen Nevis walk is an excellent bad-weather alternative if you are waiting for a clear day to ascend Ben Nevis, and the Glen Roy walk is in the same area.

I have arranged the walks as if they were being carried out in a single trip, starting in the far northwest with the alluring quartzite and sandstone hills of Arkle and the Assynt region and ending near the Highland Boundary fault gazing down on the sparkling beauty of Loch Lomond. This makes structural sense for the book, as the order of walks more or less reflects the geological journey from the three-billion-year-old ancient gneiss to the comparatively youthful 60-million-year-old igneous rocks that accompanied the birth of the Atlantic Ocean. There is of course no need for the walks to be carried out in such an order. Each walk stands on its own and they can be walked in any order and in any number. It is also intended that each walk should give the reader insight into the scenery of areas with similar geology. For example, if the weather or your own plans direct you to climb Foinaven rather than Arkle or Ben Lawers rather than Meall nan Tarmachan, the main geological lessons should still be applicable.

There is inevitably some imbalance in the coverage of various rock types. In particular, some readers may find that I have included too many hills of Torridonian sandstone and Cambrian Period rocks, and not enough of the Moine. The north-western Highlands are however not only some of the most scenically compelling parts of the Scotland, but also provide some of the most geologically fascinating oversights of the great Moine Thrust Zone.

Grading

As noted above, those familiar with the hills of England or Wales will find the Scottish hills significantly wilder, rougher and more remote. The grading system I have used (and which is borrowed and slightly adapted from R. Storer's 100 Best Routes in Scottish Mountains) offers an assessment of the navigation, terrain and general 'severity' of the walk.

The grading is relative to the other walks in this book. A grade 3 walk in Scottish terms is probably tougher than a grade 5 walk in the Peak District or a grade 4 walk in Snowdonia or the Lakes. The grade given in each case represents the hardest section on any walk, so a high navigational score may mean that only one section is difficult.

Please remember that these grades apply only in clear weather and on snow-free hills. If you risk the walks in misty or cloudy weather, the navigational challenges will increase significantly on all the walks (except for Glen Nevis and on those routes following very clear paths such as Ben Nevis, Ben Lomond and Coire Mhic Fhearchar). If you risk a route in bad weather, the whole walk will be much more demanding. If you risk it with lying snow, the walking conditions will be tougher and potentially much more dangerous.

A light dusting of snow is excellent for bringing out geological features (as is often also the case with low slanting sunlight), but any thickness of the snow blanket will smother most of those features. These geological walks are therefore really intended for summer trips rather than winter walks; shorter days and tougher conditions will not encourage readers to stop to appreciate the finer points of the rocks or the scenery.

Safety

I make no apology (except to Scottish walkers, who don't need to be told this again and again) for repeating the point that the Scottish hills are much tougher and more remote than even the toughest and most remote corners of the English and Welsh uplands. Safety should correspondingly be an important concern for walkers.

The most important safety considerations are terrain, navigation and remoteness. In the hills, a minor problem such as a twisted ankle or a broken boot can turn into a serious issue so care and prevention are vital. If things do go wrong however, the correct response is critical.

It is important to take enough clothing and food and drink to cope with sudden and dramatic changes in weather conditions and to deal with any minor problems that do arise. The conditions on Scottish mountains can change from balmy to blizzard in the blink of an eye, at any time of the year. If venturing out on the hills you must have a map and compass with you, and knowledge of how to use them. A GPS device is a useful back-up in remote spots, but is never a substitute for map and compass. A GPS may also be helpful in locating some of the locations mentioned in the walks. The grid references given in the text and walks are either six-figure or eight-figure depending on the context; the longer number is provided if finer navigation is required.

The mountain rescue is a volunteer operation and the rescuers do not get paid. Do not call them unnecessarily, but rest assured that if you really need help they will not hesitate to get that help to you. However, don't expect them to be eager to assist if you haven't bothered to take a map with you or are 'lost and late for dinner'. In the event of needing evacuation, dial 999 or 112 and ask for the police and then for mountain rescue.

Advice from the mountain rescue organisations is to keep your mobile phone switched off until you need to use it, to conserve battery power in the event of an emergency. They often find communication with those in need is hampered by flat batteries. You can register your mobile phone to use text messages to summon help. This makes sense, as texting requires less radio capacity (bandwidth) than voice communication and a text message can often get through when a voice signal is unavailable. Another (although expensive) option is to buy a satellite alarm device and subscribe to a satellite alarm service such as SPOT (Système Pour l'Observation de la Terre). This will work even if you are out of range for mobile phones.

Maps and books

This book covers a vast area and to follow all the walks would require a significant investment in OS or Harvey maps. It is however possible to buy a complete set of OS 1:50,000 maps of the whole of the UK in digital form for as little as about £70 at the time of writing. If you can spare the cash, this is excellent value. You can then print off (and laminate) the maps you need. The one disadvantage of this is that you really need to know in advance exactly where you intend to walk, which reduces your adaptability to changing conditions.

Maps can also be accessed out on the hills via GPS devices, smartphones and tablets. I haven't tried these methods so cannot comment, except to note that battery life is again an important issue (as is signal availability if maps are not downloaded in advance of use).

The biggest choice facing the walker is whether to go for 1:50,000 or 1:25,000 maps. The topography is actually much easier to read on the 1:50,000 scale maps. Sometimes it can be almost impossible to visualise the landscape depicted on the OS 1:25,000 maps because of the excess of rock outcrop markings. This is amply illustrated on Bidean nam Bean (walk 16) where the shape of the ridge is quite complex where it links with Stob Coire nan Lochan (on the descent of the recommended route). The shape is quite clear on the 1:50,000 map, but completely blurred on the 1:25,000 map. On the other hand, the 1:25,000 map has room to show much more detail in the contours and small-scale features. This is well illustrated on the ascent of the igneous ring of hills leading to Meall nan Con (walk 15). The recommended route ascends via a stony gully that is quite clearly marked on the OS 1:25,000 map, but is barely distinguishable on the 1:50,000 map.

The choice of map is therefore rather complicated and the best type may vary from place to place. I certainly recommend using the 1:25,000 map on the Meall nan Con walk on Ardnamurchan (walk 15) and for the Meall nan Tarmachan ridge (walk 17), but elsewhere it is much more a choice of which map type you prefer and/or already have available.

If you find the subject of geology interesting and want to know more about the areas where you are walking, then a geology map is a very useful tool. A good option is to buy some of the regional 1:250,000 geology maps. These do not show much local detail, but they do show the main rock types and are more useful on the ground than seems likely. Three maps cover nearly the whole of the area dealt with in this book: Sutherland, Great Glen and Argyll. The Cairngorms would require a fourth map.

For more detailed maps, there are two 1:25,000 geology maps available (both recently published) for the Highlands: Ardnamurchan Central Complex and Glen Coe. It makes sense to use the OS 1:25,000 map in conjunction with these geology maps. A dedicated book is available to accompany the Glencoe geology map – *Classical Areas of British Geology: Glencoe Caldera Volcano, Scotland* by B. Kokelaar – but is written for academic geologists.

For the rest of the Highlands, the 1:50,000 maps (or the even older one-inch to the mile 1:63,360 scale) are the only geological maps available. The age of the mapping varies, but in general they are fairly old and some date back to the beginning of the last century. It must be said that the Scottish Highlands are very poorly served by the present range of British Geological Survey maps, despite the importance of the Highlands in development of geological sciences. The maps I have used for this book are listed in Sources along with comments on their usefulness.

The dearth of good geology maps becomes a glut in one area: there are two different geology maps available for the Assynt area, both at 1:50,000 scale and both recently published. *Scotland Special Sheet Assynt* is a very detailed map showing many of the individual thrusts in the Cambrian quartzite and other rocks of the region, plus lots of other information. *Exploring the Landscape of Assynt* is a much simpler affair, showing fewer rock types and very few of the thrust lines. It is accompanied by a booklet of the same name with a few short walks (some covering parts of walks in this book). If you are unused to geology maps then the latter is probably the better option; if you want to explore the geology described in this book on the hills, however, the former will be more useful in the long run.

I have seen a smartphone and tablet 'app' which allows you to look up BGS maps to see the rock type at your location throughout Britain, opening a new (and much cheaper way) of checking the bedrock geology of wherever you are - and is ideal for amateur geologists (the only thing you really miss is the ability to see the wider picture which is often very useful). This sort of application will become much more common and even more sophisticated over the next few years and the BGS is to be congratulated on its 'free our data' approach. A phone does require batteries and signal, however, and the app is not overly detailed. For example, it did not show an outcrop of volcaniclastic sandstone we were looking at in the Lake District, although the outcrop was shown on the 1:50,000 printed map. No doubt this sort of service will become more common and improve dramatically over the next few years.

There are no really suitable geology books/guides to recommend for the Highlands as such. Those available are either ferociously technical or else cover the whole of Scotland, devoting only a small amount of space to the Highlands. Readable books in the latter category are *Geology and Landscapes of Scotland* by C. Gillen and *Land of Mountain and Flood* by A. McKirdy and co-authors (a valiant attempt to write a book about geology *and* Scotland, rather than the geology *of* Scotland). Also of interest are *Hostile Habitats: Scotland's Mountain Environment* by M. Wrightham and N. Kempe and *The Evolution of Scotland's Scenery* by J.B. Sissons (which covers glaciation).

Several good booklets/pamphlets are available. *The Landscape Fashioned by Geology* booklets are particularly useful, but it would be expensive to buy them all. Fortunately this is not essential as they can be downloaded (legally) for nothing from the Scottish Natural Heritage website (www.snh.gov.uk).

Photo w0.1 | A hail shower approaches on the lower flanks of Sgurr Mor.

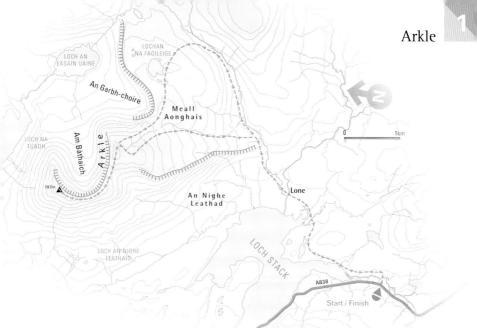

Walk #1
Arkle

START	▶	NC 296 402
FINISH	●	NC 296 402
TIME	◔	5 HOURS+
GRADE	☊	NAVIGATION ● ● ●
	☁	TERRAIN ● ● ● ●
	✈	SEVERITY ● ● ● ● ●

Arkle and its northern neighbours, Foinaven (Fionne Bhein) and Cona Mheall, form a complex mountain massif where 500 million year old Cambrian quartzite sits on top of ancient gneiss up to 3 billion years old. This age gap is worth pondering. In many places in the world, rocks from the Cambrian period would be considered ancient – in the juxtaposition with the old gneisses, however, they are mere newcomers.

Arkle

As recounted in Chapter 2, during their long lifetime the ancient gneisses have been subject to many different processes including being squeezed and heated, dropped deep down into the earth's crust and then pushed back up again to the surface. At some point, the gneiss was uncovered by erosion on the earth's surface.

Between about 540 and 500 million years ago, the area was drowned beneath a fairly shallow sea and sediments of sand, silt and mud were deposited on top of the gneiss. The seas teemed with life and many animals' remains were fossilised as the sediments suffocated and entombed them. Others were transformed into calcium carbonate deposits. Today we are left with a variety of Cambrian rocks, including quartzite, siltstone, sandstone and limestone.

In the 500 million years which have passed since then, vast earth movements caused by shifting tectonic plates have taken place. The quartzite and limestone have been broken up, with massive lumps being thrust up into a great broad pile in the Moine Thrust Zone (see Chapter 5).

Much of this earth history is visible in these attractive mountains. The division between the gneiss and the quartzite angles across the mountainsides and is easily seen on the massif, both from a distance and from close up. It is also possible to see evidence of the thrusting and piling up of the rock layers and fascinating fossils can be seen in many places.

The view of Arkle and Foinaven from the main roads is that of their fairly uniform south-western flanks. Once up on either ridge, however, vistas of the immense glacial corries that bite deeply into the mountain ridges on their north-eastern sides can be enjoyed. There are wonderful views from the mountain tops of the rough, gnarly 'knock and lochan' territory of the ancient gneisses stretching towards Cape Wrath and the Atlantic Ocean (see Chapter 2).

Foinaven is the more substantial mountain with more corries and some highly dramatic ridges, but it is also considerably more remote with long walks in and out from whichever direction it is tackled. Cona Mheall is even more remote from the west but is accessible from the northeast, offering a superb display of 'imbricated' quartzite thrusts when seen from within Strath Coille na Fearna.

Arkle has a less demanding walk in and out than Foinaven, but it is still 4km each way from the start of the walk to the start of the climb up Arkle itself. It is also a bit lower than Foinaven, so is marginally more likely to be cloud free than its taller neighbour.

On the OS 1:50,000 map, Arkle looks a bit like a beheaded and de-trumpeted version of the messenger logo that used to grace British Telecom's otherwise dull grey fleet of vans. The two 'legs', both bent at the 'knee', represent the crags below sharp edges to the plateau south of Arkle's lower summit point (spot height 758m at grid reference NC 3099 4529).

The ridge narrows considerably for a short distance north of this point, providing an exciting route to the true summit (spot height 787m at grid reference NC 3027 4616) where the ridge again widens outs. The return route re-crosses the narrow section of the ridge then diverts to the left to pass a glacially scoured lochan.

The walk starts from the parking place at the beginning of a private vehicle track about 1km north of Achfary on the A838. Follow the vehicle track for just over 3km to the bridge at Lone. Initially the views are dominated by the bulk of Ben Stack on the left (see Walk 2), but as the track swings right past the estate buildings at Airdachuilinn, the elegant form of Arkle takes pride of place.

The boundary between the underlying gneiss and the overlying quartzite is quite clear (see Photo w1.1), sloping gently towards you and reaching ground level some distance before the track. The very bottom of the quartzite is hidden by the collection of scree at the base of the crags and much of the gneiss is hidden under vegetation, but there is quite a clear shelf where the quartzite meets the gneiss.

Photo w1.1
Approaching Arkle, the layers of Cambrian quartzite can be seen resting on ancient gneiss.

Arkle

The quartzite crags lie in clear layers, generally sloping down at the same angle as the contact between the two rock types. There is a clear upwelling to the right however, above the section where the gneiss dips below surface. A closer examination of this area of quartzite shows that the beds are rather broken up in places and not as regular as further left. These are in fact signs of the 'imbrication' (see Chapter 5) or the piling up of thrusted sections of the quartzite in front of the Moine Thrust. A pair of binoculars would be useful for obtaining a good close-up view of the imbricated strata.

After crossing the bridge at Lone, take the left-hand track towards a small plantation. As you approach the wooded area, you can see a gorge over on the right where the river has cut through the steep slope of the quartzite. You only get a glimpse of the gorge here, but it is best viewed later (especially on the descent).

As you enter the wood, the track passes through two or three large 'erratics', boulders dumped by the last melting glacier in this valley. The path starts to twist and climb through the woods and continues to climb as it leaves the trees. There are some minor quartzite outcrops on the left of the track as you ascend further.

There is a small cairn on the left of the track at about grid reference NC 317 428, marking the start of a narrow path that climbs steadily up the southern flank of Arkle (initially quite muddy). Follow the path for about 150m of ascent (to about a height of 300m), then start to bear right to pick up a stream somewhere about grid reference NC 317 434. Follow the stream up to its source, passing an enchanting little waterfall/cascade in a rounded amphitheatre with a series of ledges created by the tilted 'bedding' of the quartzite. As you ascend further, you can see how the tilted bedding defines the asymmetric slanting cross-section of the stream.

Another feature that becomes increasingly evident as you ascend is the presence of 'quartzite pavement', where the tilted bedding of the rocks is exposed at the surface with a little scrappy vegetation. Quartzite has a very high proportion of quartz or silica in its make up. It is a fairly stable mineral chemically speaking, so it does not break down to provide minerals for the formation of soil and growth of vegetation. Quartzite is usually applied as a label to metamorphosed sandstone (for example in the Grey Corries and the Mamores range), but throughout the Moine Thrust Zone the Cambrian quartzite is a sedimentary sandstone with a very high proportion of quartz.

The individual layers of quartzite, exposed as pavement or in the stream bed, represent the layers of sediment laid down in succession. Its upper surface layer is known as a 'bed' and would have been a sea floor more than 500 million years ago.

Photo w1.2
Quartzite
'pavement'
on Arkle.

The pavement is far from smooth; rather, it is broken by joints which were formed when the wet sediment dried out and contracted slightly as it was transformed into rock. Millions of years later the jointing has been exploited by freeze-thaw cycles to break up the rock. Combined with the tilted bedding of the rock, this irregular jointing makes it rather awkward to walk on. The pavement is also covered with loose lumps of quartzite, broken off the main outcrop by repeated cycles of freeze and thaw (see Photo w1.2).

One particular feature of these rocks is what is known as 'pipe rock'. Often reddish in colour, the pipe rock is believed to contain the fossilised remains of worm burrows in the sand from which the rock was formed (see Photos w4.7 and w4.8). The 'pipes' are white, somewhat less than 1cm in diameter, and can be seen in outcrops and individual boulders in both plan and section views.

The pipe rock is seen on various levels as you ascend (and again on the ascent to the col between the two high points). Geologists believe that the rock occurred at only one level in the original rocks. However, it can be seen on so many different levels on Arkle because of the thrusting caused by the collision of two continental plates. The original beds have been broken and then thrust upwards above the same type of rock. Each noticeable recurrence of the pipe rock that you pass as you ascend represents another broken part of the rock that has been thrust upwards. This repeated piling up on top of itself of a layer of rock is known as 'imbrication' and is a common feature in the Cambrian quartzites and other rocks of northwest Scotland (see Chapter 5).

On reaching a height of about 700m, break away from the stream bed and bear left to reach the top of the crags overlooking the valley between Arkle and Ben Stack for tremendous views of the lake strewn area. Then aim for the highest point on this part of the mountain (spot height 758m, NC 309 453) for equally stunning views of Foinaven in the middle distance and Am Bathaich below you. This east-facing corrie has eaten into Arkle, leaving a narrow ridge circling round the top of this natural quarry (see Photo w1.3).

Photo w1.3

The glacial corrie Am Bathaich with Foinaven in the distance; note the conspicuous sloping boundary between the gneiss and the quartzite on Foinaven.

Descend from the plateau towards the col, keeping an eye out for an obvious outcrop of pipe rock. See if you can also spot the corresponding pipe rock layer on the other side of the col as you start to re-ascend. It is from this point that the ridge begins to narrow, but nowhere precipitously.

For one short section, the ridge top is defined by the gently tilting quartzite bedding (see Photo w1.4). Take care not to trip up on the knobbly rock outcrops, as your attention will inevitably be drawn to the ever more impressive views of Am Bathaich. Look at where the northern corrie wall joins the main ridge to see clear deformation folds caused by the thrusting of the broken sections of the quartzite during mountain building (see Photo 5.1). The tilted bedding underfoot is the surface expression of one of the imbricated thrusts.

The narrow section of the ridge soon comes to an end and the summit plateau widens out. Walk out for 150–200m beyond the summit cairn for super views of Foinaven's southwest flank and the underlying gneiss basement rocks stretching off into the distance. The sloping

Photo w1.4 | 'Imbricated' thrust planes on the narrowest section of the summit ridge of Arkle.

Photo w1.5 | Thrust lines in quartzite on the southern side of Am Bathaich.

boundary between the quartzite and gneiss is again very clear and it is obvious that Foinaven's north-westernmost summit point, Ceann Garbh, is entirely formed of gneiss. There are also superb views over the knock and lochan territory to the north and west (see Photo w2.2).

When you've seen enough of the distant views, it is time to turn round and re-cross the narrow ridge and the slight col between the two summit plateaux. On this return leg, the views are again dominated by Am Bathaich and Foinaven. You can clearly see the sloping quartzite strata in the corrie's southern wall, with deformation zones indicating the imbricated thrusts where the wall joins the main ridge (see Photo w1.5).

Return to spot height 758m and then head down roughly south–southeast along the edge of the plateau above another impressive corrie, An Garbh-choire. Aim for just north of Meall Aonghais, where you then swing left towards the south of Lochan na Faoileige. This is a classic glacial scouring area. The lack of vegetation on the quartzite 'pavement' emphasises the flow of large glaciers or ice sheets across this col, scraping into the rock and even scouring out a basin which is now occupied by the lochan. There would have been no vegetation at all at the end of the ice age, something which can easily be comprehended here given how little vegetation has managed to take root even after some 10,000 years.

Pick a route to join the vehicle track at about grid reference NC 334 447. Turn right and follow the track back to the starting point. As you approach the point where you left the track on the outward journey, enjoy the excellent views of the gorge cut through the hard quartzite outcrop by glacial meltwater. Savour the last views of the crags of Arkle on your right until the track turns south near the estate buildings, allowing you to enjoy the fine vistas of Ben Stack.

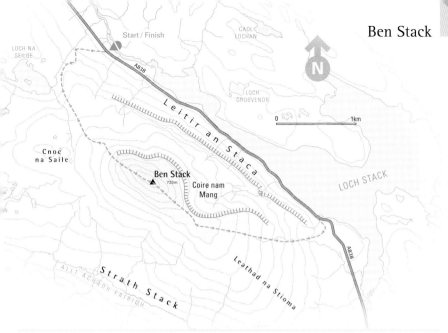

Walk #2
Ben Stack

START	▶	NC 2646 4373
FINISH	●	NC 2646 4373
TIME	☾	5 HOURS+
GRADE	⊙	NAVIGATION ● ● ● ●
	☁	TERRAIN ● ● ● ●
	⊗	SEVERITY ● ● ● ●

Ben Stack lies just southwest of Arkle (see Walk 1) and Foinaven, yet its geological structure and shape are quite different. Whereas Arkle and Foinaven owe their form to the presence of Cambrian quartzites lying on top of ancient gneisses, in the case of Ben Stack there is no quartzite. Ben Stack lies within the ancient 'basement' or 'foreland', so is somewhat unusual in being a mountain formed mainly of ancient gneiss.

Ben Stack

This is not the whole picture however, since the area to the immediate north and northwest of Ben Stack is in fact heavily intruded by numerous 'sheets' of granite. This area (running from Loch Laxford on the coast to Loch Stack immediately east of Ben Stack) was a key tectonic zone in ancient times. The area marks the boundary between two different rock systems within the ancient gneisses which formed separately before being joined during the collision of continental plates (see Chapter 2).

The granite sheets were intruded about 1.85 billion years ago. The gneiss into which the granite was intruded was originally created almost 3 billion years ago, so it had already endured over 1 billion years before the granite was intruded as sheets between layers of gneiss.

It is the inter-layering of gneiss and granitic sheets, and the fact that the inter-layered rocks have been folded upwards in later mountain-building episodes during the collision of continental plates, which have given Ben Stack its distinctive shape.

Ben Stack appears as a pyramid (see Photo 1.4) from the west. Seen more closely however, it clearly consists of a series of rock strata running roughly northwest to southeast. The way the inter-layered gneiss and granite (after being folded upwards) have since been eroded away into the present-day pattern accounts for the complex profile of the mountain. It also accounts for the double summit ridge that will be met later on.

Ben Stack has very fine views as well as interesting geology. The ancient gneiss foreland with its characteristic knock and lochan terrain is superbly seen from the summit area. There are also wonderful views of Arkle and the mountain ranges to the south and east.

The track starts just behind a building on the south-western side of the A838, just northeast of the turn off to Lochstack Lodge (NC 267 437). The well-engineered track gives an easy start to the ascent. From quite early on, you can see granite inter-layered with gneiss in the trackside cuttings and nearby outcrops. After rounding a corner you come to a cutting with good exposure of granite; the individual crystals in the granite are fairly large so they are easily distinguishable by the human eye. Further up on the track, as it rounds a bend and enters a sort of bowl, there is a large outcrop of gneiss on the left. Severe deformation folds can be seen in the rock (see Photo w2.1).

The gneiss is highly variable; some light grey, some dark grey, some with a clear layering and some of the layered rock showing deformation folds. With their light- and dark-coloured bands, the layered rocks look a bit like liquorice allsorts. You can also see fresh faces in a few places where, for some reason or other, the rock has been broken quite recently and there has been insufficient time for the forces of chemical weathering to change the colour of the rock. Fresh faces here are a dark blue, and it is worth noting that no lineation is usually visible in fresh faces. It takes the actions of chemical weathering on the different minerals to bring the lineation to our attention.

As the path approaches a stream, look out for a small cairn on the left marking the start of a rough, muddy track up towards the summit of Ben Stack. It is not possible to see the up-per reaches of the mountain when you first start on the muddy track, but the steep-looking way ahead will be revealed after a few minutes' slog.

Keep close to an old fence on your right until it starts to bend away to the right; carry straight on up from here towards the rather intimidating rocky route to the summit. The slope is not as fearsomely steep as it looks due to foreshortening of the view from this angle.

Ben Stack

Photo w2.2 | Knock and lochan topography. A distinct large-scale structural 'grain' is visible in the ancient gneiss running from the upper-left to the lower-right, marking major faults and shear zones. A less obvious grain runs from lower-left to upper-right, marking rock boundaries within the gneiss.

Before tackling the steep section, you will arrive at some gneiss outcrops where you can see the way the layers of gneiss have been 'stacked' when they were folded upwards. You then come to a slight dip where it is worth going over to the left for views of the gneiss foreland, Arkle and Foinaven. The gneiss is clearly 'grained', as can be seen in Photo w2.2 taken from this viewpoint. The grain runs directly away from the viewpoint.

Get ready to tackle the steep ascent to the summit. Although generally a 'walk', there are a few places where it will be necessary to set hand to rock and scramble/scrabble up the odd rock step. The track is fairly easy to follow, however.

The track will eventually bring you out onto a narrow, grassy ridge. Although fairly narrow, the ridge is short and is only likely to be a problem in very strong wind. Very soon the ridge broadens out and becomes the left-hand ridgeline along the summit area. There is another ridge on the right-hand side, separated by only a shallow depression (see Photo w2.3). The housing of the radio antenna on the left-hand summit bump provides useful shelter from bad weather while you appreciate the views.

The views from the summit are spectacular, especially of Arkle but also to the east and south. The gently sloping boundary between the underlying gneiss and the overlying quartzite on Arkle is particularly clear. If the weather is good, the views west and northwest across the gneiss foreland show the topography of these ancient rocks very well indeed. Particularly impressive is the vast number of little lochans separated by intricately patterned small ribs of rock.

Photo w2.3 | The double ridge line on the summit of Ben Stack.

Photo w2.4 |
Looking back towards the
summit of Ben Stack from
the descent route. The steep
tilt of the rocks is evident
both in the foreground
outcrops and on the right
face of the summit area.

The end of the summit area leads to a steepish descent on grass, although the slope soon levels out for a few minutes. The tilted rocks on the summit are best appreciated by turning round while passing through this shelf (see Photo w2.4). Looking in the direction of descent from this same area you can see the quartzite which slopes gently down from upper left to lower right, reaching low ground behind Loch Stack. The quartzite crags continue south across Srath Luib na Seilich (NC 323 416).

The remaining the descent can be fairly unpleasant if wet. Pick a route through craglets in the damp, hummocky terrain and watch out for holes underfoot. Aim to meet the road at about NC 293 416 (south of the bend in the road at NC 292 417).

Ben Stack

The idea of a road walk may not usually be very appealing, but this one is an exception for its views initially towards Loch Stack and Arkle. Soon the view becomes dominated by the prominence of Rubh Aird a' Mhadaidh and other unnamed 'knocks'. This is a very easy way to get a good close-up view of classic gneiss landscape.

Don't forget to look up at the extremely steep slopes of Ben Stack above you on the left (west). The gap between these crags and those of Arkle to the east is about 3km. Clearly some powerful valley glacier has smashed through here, with the tough rocks of Ben Stack and Arkle confining the ice and forcing it to cut downwards. It takes a bit less than an hour to walk back to the starting point, but it seems like no time at all.

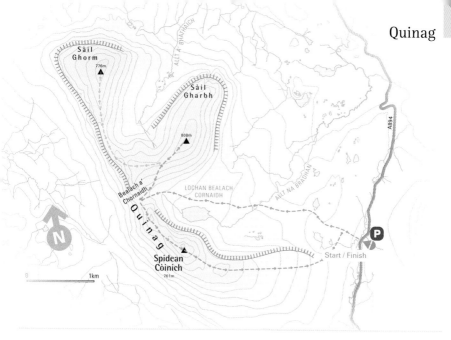

Walk #3
Quinag

START	▶	NC 232 273
FINISH	●	NC 232 273
TIME	☁	5 HOURS+
GRADE	◑ NAVIGATION	● ● ●
	☁ TERRAIN	● ● ● ●
	◈ SEVERITY	● ● ●

Quinag makes a most impressive mountain scene. Its triple arms, Sàil Ghorm, Sàil Gharbh (the highest point) and Spidean Còinich, rear up dramatically from the lower ground when seen from just about any viewpoint to the north and the east. The ridges look far too difficult for the ordinary hillwalker at first sight, but reaching the summit of Quinag on Sàil Gharbh is actually not a difficult walk (like all hillwalking,

131

this must of course be treated as a potentially very difficult walk in bad weather conditions). Some may find the recommended return route via Spidean Còinich somewhat steep in places, but it is possible to return by the outward route (the easiest track on the mountain).

One reason why the walk is comparatively straightforward is that it starts and finishes at a height of just under 250 metres above sea level – at 809m, the summit requires a modest 550m of ascent. In return for this relatively minimal effort, you are rewarded (on a fine day) with stupendous views across some of Britain's most spectacular and wild landscapes where eagles may be sighted. There are also some fascinating geological features, such as the Assynt bulge in the Moine Thrust Zone where older rocks have been pushed up above younger rocks as a result of the gigantic pressures generated by the collision of continental tectonic plates (see Chapter 5).

The view of the Glencoul Thrust from the Sàil Gharbh ridge is particularly good as you can easily spot the main thrust line over a wide area and identify the locations of the different rock types. This allows you to gain an impression of the size of the thrust zones, and therefore get an idea of the tremendous forces which must have been invoked to move so much weight over such distances.

The standard view of the Glencoul Thrust plane from a parking place on the A894 (about 5km north of the start/finish point for this walk) is certainly impressive, but it is rather like looking at a cross-section diagram. The view from the summit ridge is much more three-dimensional, allowing an overview of a much larger section of the thrust, and is the highlight of this walk from a geological point of view.

Like many mountains of the northwest Highlands, Quinag is primarily formed of dark red Torridonian sandstone and light grey Cambrian quartzite while the surrounding lower ground is mainly ancient gneiss. The bulk of the mountain is sandstone with quartzite forming the southeast ridge (Spidean Còinich), although there is also a small capping of quartzite around the main summit area (Sàil Gharbh).

Two geological maps are available of the Assynt area, both at the 1:50,000 scale but with very different levels of detail (see the information on maps in the About the Walks section of this book). If you intend to follow this walk (and Walk 4) or other walks in the Assynt area, it is well worth acquiring one of these geological maps.

The track starts directly across the road from the car parking place, initially through heather-covered quartzite. The bulk of the mountain (and especially the ridge of Sàil Gharbh) appear unassailable but, after a short while, your initial destination of the deep notch or bealach in the middle of the ridge is never out of sight. Ignore a junction in the track which goes off to the left after a couple of hundred metres (the recommended return route) and carry straight on towards Sàil Gharbh and the deep bealach (or col) to its left (west).

Although generally boggy, there are quite a few quartzite blocks littered about and small areas of quartzite pavement. The exposed sections represent the beds laid down under the sea some 500 million years ago; the tilt of the pavement shows the overall angle of the rock strata, dipping gently to the east.

Some of the exposed boulders and pavements contain examples of 'pipe rock'. These tube- or pipe-like features within the Cambrian quartzite rocks are believed to be the fossilised casts of worms that lived in the sands before it was compressed into sandstone. The Cambrian quartzite in Assynt is an un-metamorphosed sedimentary rock, but the quartzite of the Grampian Highlands (in the Grey Corries and the Mamores for example) has been metamorphosed.

After a while the greyish quartzite boulders become fewer, replaced by a mass of reddish sandstone boulders. Classic features of sedimentary rocks, such as 'bedding', 'cross-bedding' and 'graded-bedding' (see Chapter 3), can be seen as you gently ascend the corrie between the enclosing arms of Sàil Gharbh and Spidean Còinich (see Photos 3.7 and w3.1).

As you ascend into the corrie keep an eye out on the left for Lochan Bealach Cornaidh. From this level on, it is possible to see the near-horizontal layers of sandstone in front of and behind the lake (although the sandstone is replaced by quartzite on Spidean Còinich about 75m above the lake). The ascent into the corrie is in fact a series of rises over the large steps formed

Photo w3.1 │ Graded bedding
with heavier grains of sand tending
to collect at the bottom of a bed.

by the individual sandstone layers, with the layers becoming more obvious and closer to one another as you approach Bealach a' Chornaidh. It may seem to the walker that the well-known feature of the 'false summit' is here substituted by the less-familiar 'false col' phenomenon. Worry not, for the views west and southwest are worth the wait. When you arrive at the bealach the vista suddenly opens up. The bulk of the scene is made up of knock and lochan topography and is one of the widest expanses of such landscape to be seen. There are scores of tiny lochans (and a few bigger ones) as well as innumerable gneiss knolls.

Several isolated mountains rise up from the gneiss foundations on your left (when looking south). Like Quinag, these are carved out of the Torridonian sandstone; some are also capped by quartzite. This quartzite capping adds emphasis to the characteristic form of these hills and visibly shapes the summit ridge of these narrow elongated mountains. Glaciers gouged out the narrow profile as they forced their way between the isolated mountains.

When you are ready to carry on, return to just below the col (to its eastern side) to spot a fairly easy rising track which climbs diagonally up to the Sàil Gharbh ridge. The track joins the ridge at a spot marked by two small cairns. Take a careful note of this point, in case deteriorating weather suggests a direct return from the summit without a visit to the subsidiary summits of Sàil Gorm and Spidean Còinich.

Once on the ridge, turn right and cross sandstone outcrops and boulders leading to a slight dip before a final rise to the summit. On the approach to the dip the boundary between the sandstone and quartzite is quite clear, indicated by the distinct change in colour from reddish brown to medium grey, which can be seen all the way to the summit and beyond. The scree below the ridge best highlights this change. As you cross the boundary between the two rock types, you are stepping over a time gap of about 500 million years (see below).

Walk out some distance beyond the summit trig point to the northeast for the best views and a superb vantage point over the Assynt section of the great Moine Thrust Zone (see Chapter 5). A bulge developed in the thrust zone in this area, and the situation is much more complicated here than along the greater run of the Moine Thrust. The bulge (or 'culmination') means that several other thrusts and an area of imbrication have developed and, thanks to erosion, now break onto the surface. In the lower ground to the east immediately before your eyes, one of these thrusts can be seen running from left (north) to right (south).

It is worth clarifying in your mind the general geological story of the area. The basement rocks are ancient gneisses (originally igneous rocks that have been highly metamorphosed, deformed and eroded). On top of these gneisses we sometimes find Torridonian sandstone, although there was a long gap between the deposition of the gneisses (about 3 billion years ago) and the sandstones (about 1 billion years ago). Despite lying in contact with one another they are very different types of rock with very different geological histories. While the gneisses have been highly metamorphosed and deformed in the period between being laid down and the laying down of the sandstones, these latter rocks have not been metamorphosed and have only been gently tilted.

The sandstone has been completely eroded away in some areas, especially to the north and west where the views are of the low, gnarled landscape of knock and lochan topography.

The third rock type present in the area on and around Quinag is the Cambrian quartzite. This too started off life as sandstone, deposited about 500 million years ago. In some places it was deposited on top of the Torridonian sandstone and in others, where the sandstone had already been eroded away, it lies directly on top of the ancient gneiss. This complicates the picture very slightly as we lack a simple and consistent column of ancient gneiss, Torridonian sandstone and Cambrian quartzite on top of one another.

The thrusting caused by the collision of continental tectonic plates adds an even greater degree of complexity.

Viewed from near the summit of Quinag

Photo w3.2 + Diagram w3.1 | Moine Thrust Zone.

Quinag

Photo w3.3
Imbrication zone
seen on Glas
Bheinn, beyond
Lochan Bealach
Cornaidh.

From our summit ridge viewpoint it is possible to distinguish, without much difficulty, a thick layer of quartzite running from north to south across the viewpoint. To the north it can be seen above Loch Glencoul (see Photo w3.2) and to the south it can be seen running into, and forming, the gradually sloping ridge of Spidean Còinich (see Photo w3.3).

It is clear that the rocks seen lying below the quartzite must be ancient gneiss, as the landscape is knobbly and definitely not formed of the linear Torridonian sandstone – so this is one of the places where the quartzite lies directly on top of the gneiss. When we look for the top of the quartzite, where we would expect to see even younger rocks; there is in fact more ancient gneiss. The explanation is that a thrust zone has pushed ancient gneiss from further east some considerable distance to the west, thrusting it up and above the younger quartzite. This is the much photographed Glencoul Thrust (see Photo 5.2).

When you've located Glen Coul and the thrust on its far shore, you can easily follow the line of the quartzite outcrop both to the north and the south. The quartzite outcrop can also be seen where the road crosses it, dropping down from near Loch na Gainmhich towards Loch Glencoul. Where the road does a couple of zigzag bends just after passing Loch na Gainmhich, a gash can be seen in the quartzite at the outlet from the loch. Here the stream draining the loch has cut a deep gorge into the hard rock along the line of a fault; the gorge and fall can be seen by walking (with care) along the northern bank of the stream from the roadside at NC 240 295, at a bend in the road over a small bridge (see Photo 11.2). The quartzite outcrop widens markedly as it nears the base of Quinag and passes into the southeastern ridge of Quniag, Spidean Còinich.

This pattern of ancient gneiss, Cambrian quartzite and ancient gneiss stretches from east of Loch an Leathiad Bhuain (5km northeast of Loch Glencoul) to the gorge and waterfall.

South of the waterfall, a new set of rocks reaches the surface for a few kilometres; Cambrian limestone (see Walk 4). The pattern is quite different from just below the summit of Glas Bheinn (about 5km southeast of the summit of Sàil Gharbh) with a new thrust line, the Sole Thrust, which runs along the east end of the Cambrian quartzite outcrop on Quinag's eastern flank. The Glencoul Thrust is now higher up at about the 300m contour, directly below the summit of Glas Bheinn. The thrust line dips gently down to 200m height where it reaches Inchnadamph to the south.

From the slopes of Cnoc na Creige (east of Loch na Gainmhich) south to near the summit of Glas Bheinn, the rock thrust forwards is the ancient gneiss. From Glas Bheinn there are several thrusts (see Photo w3.3). The uppermost thrust brings some of the quartzite on top of itself. The next thrust down is the Glencoul Thrust, a direct continuation of the same thrust seen at Loch Glencoul mentioned above (see Photo w3.3). Below the Glencoul Thrust at this location there are several minor, dipping thrusts. These occur in the Cambrian limestone and represent an imbrication zone where several small thrusts within the same rock type have been forced up on top of one another (see Chapter 5). The upper thrusts are the oldest within this pattern.

If all this is not enough, there's also the gneiss landscape to be appreciated on the way back. When you've had enough of analysing and appreciating the northern part of the Assynt Thrust landscape, turn round and decide whether to venture onto the delightful ridge walk out to Sàil Ghorm before returning via the exciting crossing of Spidean Còinich (see Photo 3.3) or to return via the outward route. Both ridges and their tops offer fantastic views: those from Sàil Ghorm the great expanse of knock and lochan topography between Quinag and the coast some 15km away, and those from Spidean Còinich to the great sandstone mountains to the south and east and towards the hills of Assynt. Sàil Ghorm involves a wonderful up-and-down walk of about 1.5km each way, adding an hour or so to the walk.

Spidean Còinich's northern flank looks rather intimidating, but a twisty track takes you up the easiest way. Spot the boundary between the sandstone and the quartzite as you start to ascend from the dip just below the summit point. The gently sloping descent from the top of Spidean Còinich is along great expanses of exposed quartzite pavement, strewn with quartzite boulders. Watch where you put your feet as there are quite a few trip hazards, especially as the ever-changing vista will continually distract you as you make your way back to the start point.

Photo w3.4 | Reddish Torridonian sandstone in foreground, with grey Cambrian quartzite on skyline; summit of Quinag

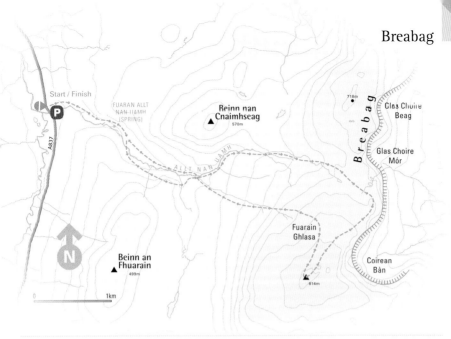

Walk #4
Breabag

START	▶	NC 253 178
FINISH	●	NC 253 178
TIME	🕐	5 HOURS+
GRADE	🧭	NAVIGATION ● ● ● ●
	⛰	TERRAIN ● ● ●
	✴	SEVERITY ● ● ●

This walk up to and on top of Breabag combines compelling views with some fascinating geology. The area's main geological interest is in the thrusts which can be found on and around Breabag in the heart of the Assynt bulge (or 'culmination') in the great Moine Thrust Zone (see Chapter 5). The bulge in the thrust zone also brings to the surface a rock known as limestone with its distinctive landscape features such as dry river valleys, cave systems, sinks and resurgence points ('karst' features in the geological lexicon). These low-level features mean that this is one of those walks where the valley approach is as interesting as the summit itself.

Indeed, the first part of the walk figures on the list of places tourists should visit and many people walk to the Bone Caves, located about 1.5km up the Allt nan Uamh valley, named for the animal bones found within the caves left there by pre-historic residents of the area. One wonders how many of those who trek up and down this short section of valley notice the odd drainage pattern or ponder reason for the dry riverbed they must cross to reach the cave.

Exactly what you will see depends on the amount of rain that has fallen in the hours and days immediately prior to your visit. If it has been dry then you will see plenty of dry riverbed, but if it has been raining for a while then you will see more of a normal flowing river, although there will still be plenty of dry sections the further up the valley you go.

The limestone dates from early in the Cambrian period (about 540 million years ago). Once you get beyond the limestone, the rocks underfoot are quartzite and were laid down later in the same Cambrian period. Both the limestone and the quartzite have been severely mashed up by the collision of continental tectonic plates, piled up into an imbrication zone (see Chapter 5). There are several imbricated thrust planes which you cross as you climb up to the summit ridge and others which can be seen in the rocks around you.

There are very fine views from the ridge of the main thrust zone of Ben More Assynt and Conival to the east and north, Canisp to the west and the gneiss/sandstone landscape of the north-western seaboard.

The Traligill valley, 3km north of the start point for this walk on the A837 at Inchnadamph, is also worth a visit as it traverses a section of a fascinating limestone valley (see Chapter 5). At one point in the Traligill valley the river descends into the limestone along the line of a thrust plane, so it is possible to kill two geological birds with one limestone by viewing both intricate karst features and gross tectonic forces (see Photo 5.5). If poor weather makes a trip to the summit ridge of Breabag uninviting, it may make sense to do two shortish walks up the Bone Caves valley and the Traligill valley.

A visit to the Knockan Crag visitor centre (just over 10km to the south on the A835) is also well worth combining with any walk in the Assynt area. The Assynt bulge is pinched out here and the Moine Thrust plane is displayed along with interpretative material (see Photos 5.3 and 5.4).

Two geological maps of the Assynt area are available, both at scales of 1:50,000 and including Breabag, although they have very different levels of detail (see the information on maps in the About the Walks section of this book). If you intend to follow this walk (and Walk 3) or other walks in the Assynt area it is well worth acquiring one or the other.

Follow the track from the car parking space, soon passing a small waterfall (at about NC 256 179). Continue up into the valley, where Cambrian limestone outcrops can be seen higher up the slopes on the left side. Boulders of limestone litter the valley floor, and you can also see examples of 'pipe rock' in the pebbles and boulders that are strewn around. The pipe rock is part of the Cambrian quartzite which forms the Breabag ridge glimpsed far ahead, so the quartzite pebbles and boulders have been carried down the valley to here. The pipes are believed to be fossilised worm tubes (see Photos w4.7 and w4.8).

The river is some way down to your right at this point, a perfectly normal noisy river. However, if the weather has been fairly dry, the river bed suddenly becomes dry at about NC 2615 1765. It should be easy to spot this point as the path has to move right up to a rock outcrop on the left and the ground underfoot is wet for a few steps (see Photo w4.1).

Do not hasten beyond this point without looking around a bit. This is where the river enters the riverbed under dryish conditions. The muddy wet patch which you have to cross supplies the river with its flow. Look to the right to see how the water flows into the river.

Rain water is slightly acidic and is made more so as it soaks through acidic mountain soil and peat. This dilute acid is sufficient to dissolve the mineral (calcium carbonate) making up limestone, so when rain and surface drainage water falls or runs onto limestone it can, over time, open up underground channels. At some point low down, the underground caves and watercourses must reach the varying level of the 'water table' or meet impermeable rocks. At whichever it meets first, the drainage water surfaces as springs such as here at Fuaran Allt nan Uamh.

If recent rainfall has been limited, the riverbed beyond this spring is dry (see Photo w4.2). After heavy rain however, the water enters the river from other higher springs and Fuaran Allt nan Uamh just adds to the overall volume of water in the river (see Photo w4.1).

Breabag

Photo w4.1 | Fuaran Allt nan Uamh (centre left) pictured after recent rainfall, adding to the flow from further up valley.

Photo w4.2 | In drier conditions, the riverbed upstream of this spring is waterless.

Before moving on, take a close look at the bottom of the rock outcrop down which water seeps. You can see a yellowish mass near the ground, which looks as if it might be a soaking wet patch of some foul viscous slime splattered against the rock face, which it is now slowly slipping down (see Photo w4.3). If you touch it however you will see that it is absolutely solid, despite its undulating drip-like profile. Small amounts of the calcium carbonate (carried in solution in the drainage water) are precipitating out of the water on coming into contact with the atmosphere. This is the same process as that which creates stalactites, stalagmites and the great sheets of calcium carbonate that form petrified 'waterfalls' in cave systems within limestone outcrops. The solid matter is called 'tufa' when it is found above ground level as here.

If the weather has been wet, you may garner some consolation from meeting another spring in action a short distance further on. At this second spring, the water appears from the middle of the valley (and not the valley side as for Fuaran Allt nan Uamh). The spring is right next to the main riverbed, but a couple of metres above it. When this spring is in flow, it feeds a small channel of its own which runs for a few metres above and parallel to the main channel before joining it. It forms a circular pool in the grass and looks deceptively calm (see Photo w4.4). From its downstream side however, a gushing flow of water tumbles fast over the pebbles (see Photo w4.5).

Photo w4.3 | A calcium carbonate deposit (tufa) precipitated from water seeping out of limestone at the Fuaran Allt nan Uamh spring.

Photo w4.4 | A spring that comes into play after wet weather, seen looking downstream.

Photo w4.5 | Looking upstream: the dry river bed can be seen above the spring, with Breabag in the far distance (top centre left). The limestone Bone Caves outcrop at top centre right.

At about NC 265 173 you need to decide whether to take a short diversion to see the caves on the way up or the way down, or not at all if your prefer (see Photo w4.6). Some of the animal bones that were found in the cave may be from animals taking shelter, but some were certainly brought in by humans and a 2000-year-old walrus ivory pin has also been recovered. The site is now protected from digging as it is a Site of Special Scientific Interest. If you visit the caves, rejoin the valley floor path by following the caves track round into a side valley on the right, then reversing direction to take you down to where the side valley meets the main valley.

Breabag

Photo w4.6 | Looking across the valley from inside one of the Bone Caves. An area of landslip is visible in the upper part of the opposite hillside, with hummocky terrain low down indicating where the slipped land has ended up. The scree is a result of more recent freeze-thaw action.

If you stick to the main track rather than visiting the caves, at one point you have to step over several drainage gullies. Keep an eye out for the rocks on the gully sides. At one gully there are two slabs of slightly reddish rock. One has short whitish streaks in it and the other small rounded whitish blobs. This is the pipe rock in section and plan, respectively (see Photos w4.7 and w4.8). Plenty more examples of both types can be seen as you progress further up to the ridge.

Also make a point of looking up towards the caves and the limestone crags above them. Here you can see great deformation zones in the limestone which represent thrust zones within the rock as it responded to the pressures of mountain building during the collision of continental tectonic plates.

At the meeting of the two valleys, follow the valley that heads up left towards the col on the Breabag ridge. You can make your way up either side of the dry river bed. There was in the past obviously quite a substantial river in the now waterless valley.

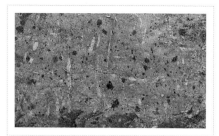

Photo w4.7 | Pipe rock seen in section; width of view approximately 60cm.

Photo w4.8 | Pipe rock seen in plan; width of view approximately 60cm.

As you walk further up the valley, the valley sides narrow quite a bit and you may well have to switch from side to side; in places you can follow the dry(ish) river bed. Eventually, depending on the amount of recent rain, you will meet a point where some water is flowing in the riverbed. It disappears from the channel without drama, as more and more of the water seeps away into dissolved watercourses below the surface. You will probably not notice exactly where you first meet water in the riverbed, but at some point there will be enough flow to attract your attention. There is no one point where it all seeps away, but as you get higher a tiny trickle slowly grows into a stream.

A bit further on you are faced with a small gorge. If you stick with the valley floor/riverbed and enter into the gorge, you will come across a fine waterfall at about NC 2754 1718. Located in the middle of a crag, it halts any direct progress for walkers. It is just possible to scrabble up the left side before the waterfall, but it is more sensible to retreat beyond the start of the gorge and ascend there to pass above the left side of the waterfall. This watefall is situated on the boundary between two types of limestone and was created by the juxtaposition of two similar rock types, but with differing resistance to erosion. This is best viewed at the base of the waterfall where the lower less-resistant rocks have been eroded away, leaving the higher tougher rocks overhanging those below.

Above the waterfall you can again make progress on either side of the river. Before long, however, you have to climb up away from the river to get above another waterfall at about NC 2793 1734. It might be more appropriate to call this a 'waterslide' rather than a waterfall but whatever name we use, the waterfall/slide is sited at yet another geological boundary, this time between limestone and sandstone. The profile of this waterfall is quite different from that of the previous waterfall – the water here cascades down sloping layers in the rock rather than pouring vertically down over an overhanging ledge. The slope represents an 'imbricated' thrust plane.

4 Breabag

From this point onwards, you are walking over the Cambrian quartzites and will encounter several sloping outcrops. You might find evidence of the origin of these rocks as sedimentary material dumped in seas or lakes, such as fossilised ripples (see Photo 4.4) just like those on a sandy beach. Some 500 million years ago that is exactly what they were but, instead of being swept away by the next tide, for some reason there was a temporary break in the cycle of deposition. This break was long enough to allow this beach to dry out sufficiently to retain the rippled surface. The cycle of deposition then resumed, and the following dumps of sediment simply rested on top of the rippled bed. Today that bed has been temporarily uncovered by erosion of the overlying rocks, and will only remain exposed until it too is eroded away.

At about NC 2855 1727 you pass a rock outcrop that you can clearly see running off to the left and the right. This is actually another outcrop of the rock encountered at the last waterfall, brought to the surface here on a thrust plane. This is the first of five such thrust planes that you cross between here and the lochan at NC 291 700. These thrust planes are shown on the British Geological Survey's Assynt Special sheet 1:50,000 geological map, but not on its simplified Exploring the Landscape of Assynt 1:50,000 map.

From this first such thrust plane you can see the bealach (col) and also, if you look both left and right (north and south) across the Breabag ridge, layers of the quartzite running across the hillside forming rock steps. The way to the col crosses such rock steps, which are the thrust planes – you will see them better from the summit ridge. Aim for the lochan at NC 291 170 and then cross the broad bealach to overlook two more lochans at NC 2965 1700 where you gain views of the valley beyond and towards Conival and Ben More Assynt, across which the Ben More and other minor thrust planes run.

When I last climbed up to this bealach, my arrival coincided with that of a sudden snow-storm charging up the slope behind me from the west. Fortunately, I found shelter behind a boulder. As the snow continued to fall I wondered if this was one of the forecast showers or the more prolonged rain which the showers it was said might merge into. Certainly, the part of the forecast which stated that the snow would be driven by a strong wind was pretty accurate. Some time later as I pondered whether my descent would be straight into the face of the snow and wind, the wind-driven downpour rose to a tremendous crescendo before rapidly dying away. I then enjoyed a nice long period before the next shower (when I was low enough for it to be rain rather than snow).

Some walkers may wish to bear up to Breabag's subsidiary northern summit (at NC 2925 1797) for immensely impressive views of Conival, Ben More Assynt and Garbh Choire. Otherwise, head southwest from the bealach to find a route between rock outcrops and

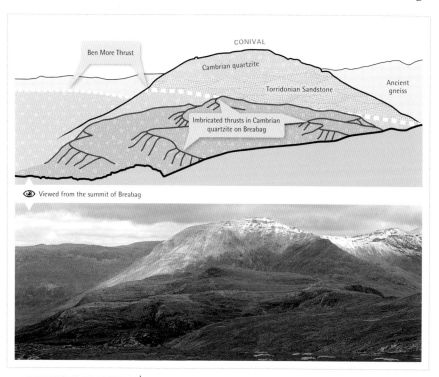

Viewed from the summit of Breabag

Photo w4.9 + Diagram w4.1 │ Imbrication thrusts seen on the bealach on Breabag. Centre rear: Conival; upper right corner: Ben More Assynt.

mounds. There are plenty of false summits on this 1.2km walk. However, instead of the usual style of false summit where you gain a rise only to see another rise directly ahead, on this ridge you see what looks like the highest of mounds ahead, clamber up to its top and see another higher mound off to one side. On reaching that mound, the process is continued.

As you ascend, take the opportunity to turn round and look at the subsidiary summit plateau of Breabag and its lines of rock (see Photo w4.9 and Diagram w4.1). These are thrust planes or, to be a bit more accurate, the bottom of each rock step sits on a thrust plane. This type of collection of closely spaced thrust planes is known as imbrication (see Chapter 5) as the rock strata continually break up, with more layers being pushed up on top to form a pile.

Try to keep well to the left as you near the summit for superb views down into Coirean Ban on your left (see Photo w4.10). More thrust planes, part of the pattern of imbrication in the piling the quartzite up on top of itself, can be seen in the right-hand corrie wall. On the

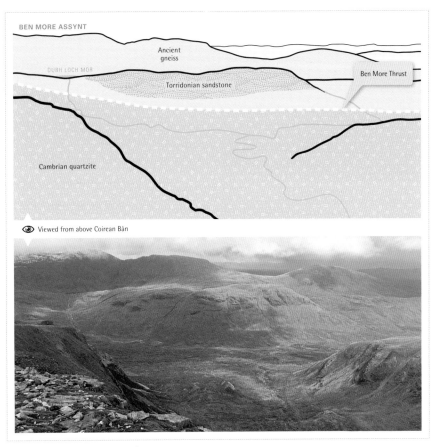

BEN MORE ASSYNT

Ancient gneiss

DUBH LOCH MOR

Torridonian sandstone

Ben More Thrust

Cambrian quartzite

👁 Viewed from above Coirean Bàn

Photo w4.10 + Diagram 4.2 | View over Coirean Ban from near the summit of Breabag. On the skyline: Ben More Assynt (left), Carn nan Conbhairean (centre) and Meall an Aonaich (right); the Ben More Thrust passes through the middle of the scene.

other side of the valley on the lower slopes of Carn nan Conbhairean and Ben More, a major thrust line can be seen that brings the ancient gneiss (up to 3 billion years old) on top of the Cambrian quartzite (500 million years old). There are also a few patches of Torridonian sandstone (about 1 billion years old) in with the gneiss, sitting on top of much younger quartzite.

The all-round views from the (rather inadequate) summit shelter are magnificent, especially to the western side with views of the Torridonian sandstone mountains poking up from the ancient gneiss basement (see Photo w4.11 which shows a sample of pipe rock found on

Photo w4.11 | Pipe rock seen in boulder forming the summit shelter of Breabag, looking west. The mixed western Assynt landscape of ancient gneiss, Torridon sandstone and Cambrian quartzite can be seen in the background with Canisp and Suilven in the distance.

the shelter in the foreground and, blurred, Canisp and Suilven in the distance).

To descend from the summit it is highly advisable to head first just west of north and then west to the head of a stream (shown at NC 283 165). Do not head northwest as there is an awkward rock face barring the way. You will in any event be guided to the north by outcrops just below the summit but, once they relent, resist the apparent attractions of a direct route and head to the steam. As you descend north you will have good views of the lines of thrust planes and rock steps on the northern summit plateau of Breabag as you descend towards the top of the stream (see Photo w4.9).

Once you reach the stream, bear left and descend on its right-hand side, steeply at first through crags and boulders. At the base of this steep section, look south along the western flanks of Breabag to see the steeply sloping and convex-curved quartzite pavement running across the hillside. The outcrop is only lightly marked on the OS map and the marking stops well before the stream, so you would get no idea of the presence of such a hazard from above. Having avoided this interesting feature, continue down near the stream picking the least-difficult terrain.

Cross out of the quartzite and back into limestone territory at around NC 2750 1685. Keep an eye on the stream and note when it begins to seep away into the riverbed. There is no sudden sink, but a gradual diminution of volume of water in the stream until it is all gone.

Breabag

Depending on the level of recent rainfall, it may appear and disappear a couple of times. Stream-spotting can compete for your attention with enjoying the stupendous views and watching where to put your feet as you descend the last section of rough hillside to rejoin the outward track near the junction of two valleys. From there head back to the beginning, past the springs and dry/wet riverbed of the outward journey.

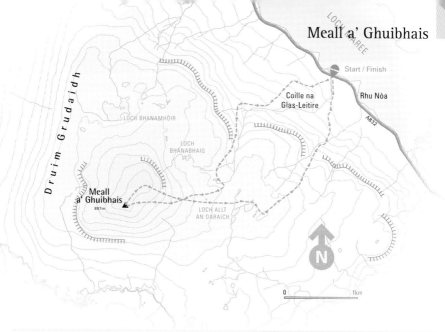

Start / Finish

Coille na
Glas-Leitire

Rhu Nòa

LOCH BHANAMHÒIR

LOCH
BHANABHAIG

Meall
a' Ghuibhais
887m

LOCH ALLT
AN DARAICH

Druim Grudaidh

N

0   1km

Walk #5
Meall a' Ghuibhais

START	▶	NH 001 650
FINISH	●	NH 001 650
TIME	◖	5 HOURS+
GRADE	◉	NAVIGATION ● ● ●
	☁	TERRAIN ● ● ● ●
	✖	SEVERITY ● ● ●

I have broken my rule about following the spelling of names as used on OS maps. On the computerised 1:50,000 map spelling is Meall a' Ghiuthais, but here I use the spelling Meall a' Ghuibhais since this is used in all other maps and guidebooks. This includes the OS computerised gazetteer which accompanies the computerised map, and which does not recognise the spelling used on the map itself.

Meall a' Ghuibhais

Meall a' Ghuibhais is a rather odd mountain. Plenty of the hills around it are made of Torridonian sandstone topped by Cambrian quartzite. Indeed, one of the best geological views on this walk is of the northern flank and buttresses of Beinn Eighe (see Photo w5.3). On Beinn Eighe the quartzite is clearly seen dipping gently down to the east, lying on top of the reddish-brown coloured sandstone. On Meall a' Ghuibhais however, the pattern is reversed and the old Torridonian sandstones (up to 1 billion years old) sit on top of the younger quartzite (about 525 million years old).

Another superb geological viewpoint is across Loch Maree to Slioch (see Photos w5.1 and 2.8). Here the Torridonian sandstone lies on top of the ancient gneiss (originally formed between 2.5 and 3 billion years). You can clearly see the undulating shape of the ancient gneiss landscape about 1 billion years ago, before the sandstone was deposited. Its neighbour Beinn a' Mhuinidh (northeast across Loch Maree) has even older rocks in the form of ancient gneiss lying on top of younger Cambrian quartzite.

This walk explores the topsy-turvy geology of the mountain landscape in this area. It makes use of the excellent Mountain Trail, maintained in good condition by Scottish Natural Heritage, which begins and ends at the Beinn Eighe car park (NH 001 650 on the loch side of the road). A guide to the natural history of the trail can be obtained from the Beinn Eighe visitor centre (NH 019 629), located 2.5km south of the recommended start/finish point on the mountain side of the road. Many guidebooks suggest using the Pony Path, but this is because they tend to assume that you will want to climb both Meall a' Ghuibhais and Ruadh-stac Beag in pursuit of ticks on a list. However, this makes for quite a substantial peak-bagging walk with little time for appreciating the rocks and the scenery.

You could still use the Pony Path to climb Meall a' Ghuibhais alone as the path takes you to the bealach (col) between the two tops, also reached on the recommended route. From a geological point of view however, the Pony Path is much less interesting than the Mountain Trail. Much of the Pony Path is simply a narrow track through dense heather, although there are of course plenty of appealing vistas.

The Mountain Trail is, all in all, a much more satisfying day out. The final part of the ascent, from the bealach to the summit and back, is trackless and a bit steep in places. Very careful navigation would be needed if the mist were to descend while on the summit. The walk can be cut short by not visiting the summit and sticking with the Mountain Trail.

From the loch side car park, take the underpass beneath the A832 and follow the path up, ignoring the footbridge on your right shortly after leaving the underpass (this will be your return route). The track passes through a gorgeous tranche of woodland, there being no grazing allowed within the nature reserve.

After a short while you will meet a cemented cairn with the word 'woodland' on an attached sign. This refers to information in the SNH Beinn Eighe Mountain Trail guide booklet, and several such cairns will be encountered. On meeting this first sign, look upwards to see quartzite crags ahead. Further on, once the track nears a stream on the left, it starts to climb fairly steeply through tilted quartzite rock steps. The ascent is not too bad, but it would be an unpleasant descent route.

On reaching the cairn labelled with the word 'geology', the SNH trail guide booklet describes the view to Slioch and discusses its geology. My recommendation however is to carry on climbing for the time being, until you reach an area more suitable for sitting down and studying the views. Continue upwards on the sloping rocks until the path takes you up onto a flattish area behind a slightly higher rock outcrop. Shortly after this outcrop, once you have a good view of Slioch and the hills to its right, find somewhere to enjoy the magnificent vista and its geology.

The top of Slioch is made of Torridonian sandstone, but this sits on a base of ancient gneiss. The gneiss was originally created from around 3 billion years ago, before undergoing metamorphosis. These metamorphic rocks were then exposed on the surface and were subject to millions of years of erosion by wind, water and ice, leaving an undulating landscape. A small part of this undulating surface is visible underneath the Torridonian sandstone (see Photos w5.1 and 2.8; see also Chapter 2).

Photo w5.1

Quartzite pavement in the foreground with lots of jointing. Looking towards Loch Maree and Slioch, an ancient gneiss valley filled with overlying Torridonian sandstone.

Meall a' Ghuibhais

Later tectonic activity led to stretching of the continental plate as it started to 'rift' and crack. The ancient gneiss landscape dropped downwards and great rivers crossed it, depositing pebbles and sandy sediment. The subsidence continued for some time so that great thicknesses of sand were laid down, which slowly transformed into sandstone. Later on the area was once again pushed upwards and subject to erosion.

To the right (southeast) of Slioch is the deep gash of Gleann Bianasdail and the angular hill to its right, Beinn a'Mhuinidh. Here you can see quartzite forming the outcrops at the top of the steep slope from Beinn a' Mhuinidh down into Gleann Bianasdail. The summit area itself is partly more gneiss and partly more Torridonian sandstone. These older rocks have been thrust up on top of the younger quartzite by the forces of collision of continental plates (see Photo 2.8).

Return to the slog upwards. Look out for outcrops of 'pipe rock' and 'trumpet rock' as you climb – these are thought to be fossil traces of creatures that lived in the sand over 500 million years ago (see Photos 4.7, 4.8 and w5.2).

Photo w5.2 | A band of pipe rock can be seen in the lower part of the photo; in the upper bands the quartzite can be seen breaking up into angular pebbles along jointing lines.

The climb becomes somewhat less steep once the track leaves the stream that you've more or less followed since near the end of the woodland. Eventually you come out on to a gently undulating/hummocky flat area with numerous small rock mounds and lots of bare quartzite. 'Pavement' would not really be the right word for such an awkward surface for walking – awkward because of the inevitable ups and downs of any route through this rockscape.

You soon reach the highest point on the Mountain Trail at a height of 550m, at about NG 9930 6330, in the midst of the wide area of quartzite outcrops. The location is marked by a 360° view symbol on modern OS maps and, indeed, the views are very fine (although not as magnificent as those awaiting you on the summit).

As the height of Meall a' Ghuibhais is 887m, the trek to the summit is only another 350m of ascent and you are well over halfway up the hill. If weather conditions such as cloud or high wind make an attempt on the top appear unwise, simply follow the Mountain Trail roughly northwest past several small lochans for about 800m, until the path starts to descend to the northeast at about NG 9872 6383.

To carry on to the summit from the cairn at the high point of the Mountain Trail either head southwest to pass Loch Allt an Daraich to its south then bear north of west to the base of Meall a' Ghuibhais, or carry on along the Mountain Trail until you have passed the lochan and then bear west. The aim in either case is to pick a route of minimum effort across the quartzite outcrop area heading towards the western end of the hill. The western slope is initially a steepish slog up grass, but increasingly over rocks and scree as it becomes steeper. Keep the main rock outcrops well to your right.

The slope becomes uncomfortably steep in places between the 700 and 800m contours, and you can slip back down the scree as much as you step upwards. With care and a little effort, this section is soon overcome and the slope eases off as you approach the summit plateau. You are immediately rewarded with exceptionally good views to the north and east over the great road-less tracts of Letterewe, Kinlochewe, Fisherfield and Strathnasheallag Forests.

Cross the 400m of the summit plateau, while enjoying views to the northwest, to reach the main summit where there is an impressive cairn/shelter. Here there are exceptionally fine views over Ruadh-stac Beag – which seems so close – and behind it the main mass of Beinn Eighe, one of Scotland's most cherished mountains (see Photo w5.3).

Photo w5.3 | Beinn Eighe seen from Meall a' Ghuibhais; An Ruadh Stac in centre foreground, with tilted quartzite lying on Torridonian sandstone.

Meall a' Ghuibhais

The dipping rock strata of Ruadh-stac Beag are particularly impressive. The dip is most apparent in the upper part of the mountain in the light-grey quartzites, although the strata are not uniformly parallel with slight variations in dip. There are in fact three thrust zones within the quartzite here, which can be seen in the three main divisions of these north-facing crags.

On the main mass of Beinn Eighe the division between the upper capping of quartzite is quite distinct from the underlying Torridonian sandstone, especially on the far right-hand spur of the mountain (Ruadh-stac Mor). The Torridonian sandstone on that spur shows very clear, almost horizontal, strata.

The mountain on which you are standing has a reverse arrangement, however, with quartzite lower down and Torridonian sandstone above. The answer to this odd situation is found in the great thrusts generated by mountain-building forces during the collision of continental tectonic plates (see Chapter 5). As well as the thrusts visible in the quartzite on Ruadh-stac Beag (and on the hills across Loch Maree to the east of Slioch earlier in this walk), thrusting also accounts for the presence of the older Torridonian sandstone on the summit of Meall a' Ghuibhais on top of younger quartzite lower down.

Having contemplated these gross tectonic forces applied over several million years a few hundred million years ago, we can shift our attention to more recent matters and the few thousand years since the end of the last glacial period. When the last glaciers melted they would have left nothing but bare rock, much of which has since become vegetated. The Torridonian sandstone is partly vegetated, but the low-lying quartzite forms the very bare area below us. The quartzite provides fewer nutrients for plants (quartz or silica being chemically fairly inert), so the area lacks much vegetation. The result is a rather barren image which gives us an idea of how the mountains as a whole would have looked at the end of the ice age (see Photo w5.4).

The particular pattern of ups and downs in this sparse landscape is the result of ice gouging out the rock more easily at boundaries and weaknesses within the rock. Some rough 'grain' of the land is distinguishable, but superficially it looks rather random with a scattering of lochans and large puddles as well as innumerable humps, each with its own skirting of scree (rather like small-scale versions of Ruadh-stac Beag).

The overall result is an unworldly vista, often compared with a moonscape. Indeed, the lochan at NG 987 637 has been dubbed 'Lunar Loch', despite the incongruence of naming a lake after a landscape that is entirely lacking in lakes. 'Glacial Loch' might be a more appropriate name.

Before leaving the summit take time to enjoy the views west over Torridonian hills

Photo w5.4 | Quartzite provides little nourishment to vegetation
(centre) compared to the Torridonian sandstone (foreground)

such as the sloping plateau of Beinn a'Chearcaill. Lacking a tough cap of quartzite, the hill has been sculpted along the near-horizontal rock strata. We should also note the views to the southeast, to the ice-scoured landscape of Bidein Clann Raonaild/Carn Loisgte south of Kinlochewe.

To descend, head down to the slight col on the summit plateau and then head roughly east of south as best as possible, picking a route down through boulders and scree. The most difficult section is once again soon over. It is then a matter of picking a route back to the Mountain Trail (which can be seen from higher up), aiming to meet it at about NG 9885 6370, although the lie of rock outcrops may push you a bit to the east.

If descending from the summit of Meall a' Ghuibhais in the mist, great care must be taken. It will be difficult to hold accurately to a bearing on the steep descent and then across the up-and-down rockscape to find the Mountain Trail. Take care not to head too far south towards the area between the highest point on the Mountain Trail and the Pony Path.

After reaching the Mountain Trail, it initially heads northwest then descends steeply to the northeast on a well-maintained path with a stream some way off to the right. Soon you enter into a steep, deep valley that has been cut into a fault line. It is also close to the boundary between the Torridonian sandstone and some Cambrian 'dolomitic siltstone' (laid down shortly after the widespread Cambrian quartzite). The rock boundary is actually part of the thrust zone which pushed the older Torridonian rocks above the younger Cambrian rocks, as discussed above.

The dolomitic siltstone is known to geologists as the 'Fucoid Beds'. Siltstone is a sedimentary rock comprising particles of silt (which are smaller than grains of sand and bigger than grains of mud). Dolomite is a limestone in which chemical processes have replaced the calcium carbonate with magnesium carbonate. This 'dolomitic siltstone' was once a rather impure limestone with lots of silt mixed in.

The stream has dug a gorge into the deep groove of the valley, but it is difficult to see down into the gorge until some way lower down the valley where the stream turns sharp right. Just beyond the sharp turn you can gain very impressive views into a considerable length of the gorge by looking back up its course. It is hard to say whether it is best regarded as a single waterfall or a series of waterfalls.

The trail continues with superb views of Slioch. At about NG 997 649 the signed track turns sharp left, but you may wish to bear right for a shorter and more direct route back to the footbridge and underpass near the car park.

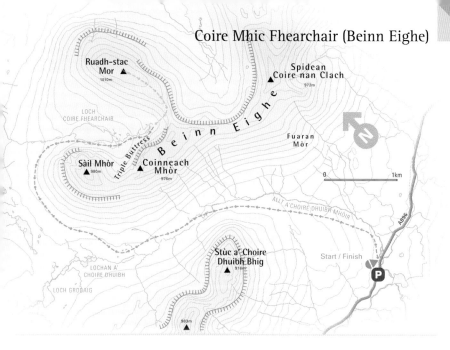

Walk #6
Coire Mhic Fhearchair (Beinn Eighe)

START	▶	NG 957 568
FINISH	●	NG 957 568
TIME	🕐	6 HOURS+
GRADE	🧭	NAVIGATION ● ●
	⛰	TERRAIN ● ● ●
	✴	SEVERITY ● ● ●

Coire Mhic Fhearchair is one of the most impressive glacial corries in the Scottish Highlands. Even though it is a two-hour walk from the road, it is one of the most accessible thanks to a very well-engineered track. This makes it a relatively easy walk with an utterly magnificent destination. The recommended walk simply follows the track round into the corrie, passing initially between Beinn Eighe and Liathach

Coire Mhic Fhearchair (Beinn Eighe)

(another impressive mountain of Torridonian sandstone) then round behind Beinn Eighe in its most remote north-western reaches.

The recommended route explores the corrie between the point where the track reaches it and its far corner, where the easiest route to the summit can be found. It then returns to the start/finish point using the same route.

In terms of navigation, if you stick to the track you would have to work very hard to get lost. If you go beyond the track to explore the corrie (as recommended), navigation could be more challenging if the mist descends. If you ascend the mountain summit, you take on some potentially serious navigational challenges and the risk of easily going off route (even in clear conditions), unless you take great care in identifying a safe and practicable downwards route.

Start at the car park at NG 957 568 on the A896 road and follow the track which initially heads towards a stream (which passes under the road). Very soon the track starts to swing left (north) and to rise steadily into the valley, Coire Dubh Mor. It is worth noting that 'coire' (corrie) can refer to both a mountain valley (i.e. not necessarily a glacial corrie) as well as the seat of a corrie glacier (the destination of the walk). Although a mountain valley, Coire Dubh Mor would of course have taken some of the ice which flowed out of the glacial corries on the northern flank of Liathach. Initially, however, it is the rounded buttress of Liathach's eastern end and the southern flank of Beinn Eighe which dominate, rearing high and impregnable on either side of you.

The top of Beinn Eighe is clearly made up of very light-coloured rock (Cambrian quartzite) while the lower slopes (as well as the eastern buttress of Liathach) are made up of older Torridonian sandstone. The quartzite areas are distinguished by the presence of much scree, while the sandstone is identifiable by the near-horizontal layering or strata.

Don't forget to turn around every now and again to enjoy views of the mountains south of the road. Most impressive is Sgurr Dubh (NG 979 557), where thrusting (see Chapter 5) has disturbed the strata.

Eventually you come to the stream crossing with its incongruously tiny stepping stones. After crossing the stream, a natural amphitheatre comes into view high up on the left below the easternmost summit of Liathach, Stuc a' Choire Dhuibh Bhig. Looking fairly horizontal, the layers of sandstone give the appearance of a human-made structure such as a Roman amphitheatre. This illusion is fully quashed by various irregularities as you go further, and it is clear that the structure of the corrie is entirely linked to that of the rest of the mountain.

This amphitheatre shape is common to a lot of corries cut into the Torridonian sandstone (you will see more such corries on Liathach further on and on Walk 7 of this book on Beinn Bhan in Applecross). As you ascend further into the valley the sides close in on you as you head towards the highest point, a glacial breaching point between Liathach and Beinn Eighe.

You can see a feature known as 'cross-bedding' on some of the rocks and boulders. This is created when sands are deposited in fast-flowing currents which create ripples or sloping beds. At some point the current shifts and the old ripples are cut off as new ripples are laid at a slightly different angle (see Photo w6.1).

Photo w6.1 | Cross-bedding on a glacially dumped block of Torridonian sandstone at the base of the slope up to the summit ridge of Beinn Eighe. Layered beds of sandstone are visible higher up the slope.

Some outcrops and boulders will contain pebbles of all sizes (not just sand) cemented together in the sandstone. Another feature you might notice is the presence of sand on the track. The sand has been released from the sandstone by chemical weathering of surface layers of rock. The cement which held together the grains of sand is attacked by the atmosphere and by rainwater. The sand grains of sand fall onto the surface, where they can be whipped up by the wind, aiding the physical erosion of the mountain and often carving lumps of the remaining sandstone into incredible shapes.

Another kilometre takes you to the highest point in the valley, where the vista opens up dramatically to the west along to Beinn Dearg and beyond it to the shapely Ben Alligin. You also obtain marvellous views from this point of the central and western corries of Liathach (see Photo 11.9).

Coire Mhic Fhearchair (Beinn Eighe)

As you head further round towards Coire Mhic Fhearchair, the views change to a wasteland of lochans and outcrops filling the area between the sandstone mountains to the west and northwest. Beinn A' Chearcaill, Beinn an Eoin and Baosbheinn are particularly impressive.

These views will occupy your mind as you continue to plod up the excellent track, which eventually steepens for the final 100m of ascent. The northern end of Ruadh-stac Mor will come into view, getting larger and larger. As you get nearer to the corrie, the view ahead is dominated by the layered rock step into the corrie and the waterfalls cascading down it.

The corrie is hidden until you finally come over the rock bar holding in the lochan, when the magnificent corrie and its striking backwall come suddenly into view (see Photo w6.2). The backwall will immediately draw the attention of anyone interested in geology, for here is one of the most obvious rock boundaries that you will see anywhere. The three great buttresses of the corrie backwall are clearly divided into two rock types with a boundary that slopes gently up from left to right. The light-coloured upper rocks are the younger Cambrian quartzites and the darker lower rocks are the older Torridonian sandstone.

Photo w6.2 | The corrie backwall with red-brown Torridonian sandstones clearly overlaid by light-grey Cambrian quartzite.

The lower slopes of the corrie backwall are covered by scree and vegetation which has grown on top of the scree. There are three 'active' scree slopes – one under each of the great gullies that scar the crags and divide into buttresses, where the continuing fall of loose rock has overwhelmed any attempts by vegetation to colonise the scree slope. Even with the scree and vegetation-covered scree, it is possible to distinguish the layers of sandstone cut almost like a staircase.

Coire Mhic Fhearchair (Beinn Eighe)

You will no doubt want to explore around the rock bar holding in the lochan and savour the fine views into the corrie and to the hills and wilderness to the north. If you want to explore further into the corrie, follow the track which sticks fairly close to the edge of the lochan on its right-hand side. There is a large boulder field at the start of the route, the result of a massive rockfall way up above you. Plenty of very clear cross-bedding can be seen in the rocks at the bottom of the fall.

Make your way across a few sections of jumbled boulder field until you soon reach the grassy areas at the back of the corrie, with magnificent views of the buttresses and the scree fans at their base.

Continue round the corrie while moving away from the lochan, climbing up through the sandstone rock steps, towards the base of the scree slope which runs up to meet the ridge at its lowest point. This is a delightful place to roam with innumerable rock steps, easy scrambling, magnificent views and an enticing atmosphere.

The rock steps are in fact wider than they look from below. Several shelves feature tiny lochans, although in general they get smaller as you climb higher (see Photo w6.3) and eventually becoming little more than puddles. The shelves grow narrower as you climb. You can see that more layers are hidden by scree and vegetation at the base of the quartzite. The view north from the higher of the steps is truly wonderful and gives a real feel for the massive size of this corrie (and thus of the glacier that would have been seated here).

Photo w6.3 | The view northwards towards Beinn a' Chearcaill from the back of the corrie, looking across the rock bar holding in the lower lochan.

Coire Mhic Fhearchair (Beinn Eighe)

The scree slope provides the route up onto the summit ridge. If you do climb up onto the summit ridge from Coire Mhic Fhearchair, it is worth visiting both the highest point (Ruadh-stac Mor) at 1010m and the subsidiary summits of Coinneach Mhor (976m) and Spidean Coire nan Clach (993m). Access to Sàil Mhòr (at 980m) is also possible, but a 'bad step' or exposed scramble has to be negotiated if you wish to get on to Coinneach Mhor from Sàil Mhòr (or the other way round). Similarly, if you venture east of Spidean Coire nan Clach you will need a good head for heights and experience at exposed scrambling.

After tackling the main ridge or the summit, the out and back route via Coire Mhic Fhearchair (while quite a long trek) is the easiest and least vertigo-inducing. There are however a couple of routes down via Coire an Laoigh (very steep and leaving you with a 2km walk back along the road) or on the south-western flank of Spidean Coire nan Clach (Fuaran Mor) direct to the river bridge near the car park.

If you miss out the summit, retrace your route or follow a variation back to the corrie lip and then follow the path back. Going in this direction, the western corries of Liathach are seen in excellent form. You may notice the hummocky terrain of the low ground near the col with Coire Mhic Nobuil. This is a feature you will notice quite commonly as you retrace the kilometres back to the car park. You may also notice a fenced-off gorge containing the stream on your left as you near the end of the track not far from the road.

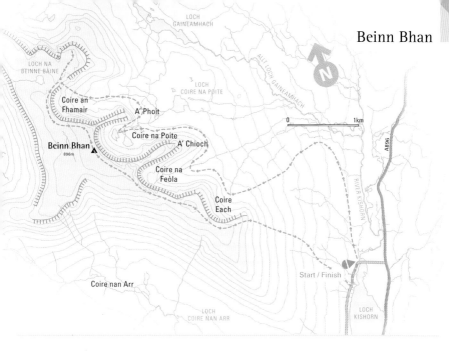

Walk #7

Beinn Bhan

START	▶	NG 834 423
FINISH	●	NG 834 423
TIME	⏱	4 HOURS+
GRADE	⊕	NAVIGATION ● ● ●
	⛰	TERRAIN ● ● ● ●
	⚡	SEVERITY ● ● ● ●

Beinn Bhan lies on the eastern side of the beautiful, fan-shaped Applecross peninsula. Its main geological interest lies in the run of glacial corries carved into the eastern flank of the mountain. The corries can be glimpsed high up on the hillside from the A896 between Ardarroch and Shieldaig. Even from this distance they look mightily impressive. The recommended route takes you right up into the corries where their

Beinn Bhan

full scale and majesty is displayed to perfection.

The uplands of south-eastern Applecross have a distinctly asymmetric profile. The western slopes are largely steep and grassy, but great voids have been cut into the mountain side on the eastern flanks of Meall Gorm, Sgurr a' Chaorachain and Beinn Bhan. From the distant hills to the south, Meall Gorm and Beinn Bhan look rather like waves frozen in the act of crashing. This is a most dramatic example of how in Britain glacial corries usually develop on the north-eastern aspect of a mountain massif.

The prevailing wind in the ice age was the same as today – from the west. Snow from the plentiful storms blowing in off the Atlantic was carried up the smooth western slopes and across the top of the uplands to collect in any sheltered hollow on the eastern side. The eastern side of the mountain also experienced less sunshine, so aiding the process of the transformation of the gathering snow into glacial ice.

The summit points of Sgurr a' Chaorachain (776m) and Meall Gorm (710m) can both easily be reached from around the highest point on the Bealach na Ba road that runs from the start point for this walk to the hamlet of Applecross on the west coast. The corries of Coire a' Chaorachain and Coire na Ba are not as atmospheric as the corries of Beinn Bhan, however. Coire na Ba is about 3km long and its atmosphere is necessarily compromised by the presence of the narrow but still busy road (it being a popular tourist drive). The corrie has an interesting profile, with upper and lower corries divided by a steep rock step and crags between the 260m and 350m contour lines. This is the result of an upper glacier cutting out the higher corrie when temperatures were rising and glaciers could only exist high up. Coire a' Chaorachain is half the length of Coire na Ba, but is still very large and fairly uniform. It is in effect the upper corrie of Coire nan Arr.

The four corries on Beinn Bhan seen from above and below on the recommended route (and a fifth corrie seen from above only) are much smaller than Coire na Ba. This combined with interesting shapes gives these corries more atmosphere and scenic interest. There is the added advantage that the Coire a' Chaorachain and Coire na Ba can both be seen from the summit ridge of Beinn Bhan, while those of Beinn Bhan are invisible from the west. Beinn Bhan is also the higher summit (by 120m) and offers more extensive all-round views, including a superlative vista of Skye in the near distance.

Parking space can be found on the side of the minor road just before the bridge. As you walk towards the bridge, note the position of the small quarry behind the bridge and road (as you will need to remember to head to either the south or north of this quarry when returning at the end of the walk). The quarry exposes the Torridonian sandstone, the only rock type to be seen on this walk.

Cross the bridge and turn right onto the track which heads initially almost due north, rising only very gently. After a while you start to gain views of the southern corries way up to your left (west). Carry on along the track until you meet a most un-usefully placed footbridge which appears to have been dumped across the track. There are several places in the Highlands where a footbridge would actually be useful so maybe, despite its aged look, it is only here temporarily and will not be in this spot in the future. If so, you will need to work out your own spot to leave the track and head up to Coire Each, which should be done roughly somewhere between grid reference NG 835 437 and NG 834 441. Bear left onto pathless terrain to head roughly west. Pick the route of least difficulty across hummocky terrain heading directly up towards Coire Each, the southernmost of the corries.

There is no track and you will either have to move left and right at different times to minimise the amount of ascent and avoid damp sections, but (as long as the corrie is not obscured by mist or cloud) the objective remains in view throughout. Foreshortening makes the corrie look closer than it is, and the 350–400m ascent is quite demanding given the rough terrain.

The slope gets steeper as you get closer to the corrie, with a final steep section taking you over the 'lip' of the corrie and into Coire Each. The crags of the corrie backwall, and especially of the rounded buttress separating Coire Each from Core na Feola, are pretty impressive. Go some way up into the corrie for the best impression of the crags to the right (north), although these give way to less striking and less craggy slopes on the left. Remember to turn around and enjoy views of the mountains off to the east.

One feature that occurs quite commonly in and below all the corries mentioned in this walk is the 'lateral moraine', formed from material dumped alongside glaciers coming out of the corrie. In the case of the Beinn Bhan corries, most of the moraines are arranged in lines which flow out from the corries. The lines vary in length and height; some stretch only a few metres while others are over 500m long. These moraines are generally narrow and can seem more like human-made mounds than ice-formed hummocks. The general trend for these lateral moraines is west–east, but some of those from Coire an Fhamair actually show that the glacier from this corrie spread up towards Loch Gaineamhach.

Beinn Bhan

There are more moraines lying at 90° to the others on the far side of Allt Loch Gaineamh-ach. It is thought that the glacier(s) in the Beinn Bhan corries stretched only just beyond that swarm of roughly north–south-trending moraines.

Work your way round the base of the buttress into Coire na Feola. Apart from the views to the east, the main point of interest is the architecture of the layered sandstone crags. This rounded buttress and the rounded corries are typical of corrie structure on the mountains of northwest Scotland that are made of Torridonian sandstone (see Walk 6 for examples on Liathach).

The sandstone is marked by distinct 'beds' or strata, each representing a period of sedi-mentation. The beds are often quite different from each other, some displaying such features as pebble beds as well as sandstone beds, cross-bedding (see Chapter 3) and ripples. These are original 'depositional structures' and the variations show geologists the different envi-ronments in which the different beds were laid down (cross-bedding features being found in areas with strong currents). This in turn allows geologists to construct a picture of the geological history of the earth through the ages.

Erosion by chemical weathering and by freeze-thaw cycles in cold conditions has gone to work on the rock and prized open 'joints' (formed when the wet sandy sediments dried out and contracted slightly during the transformation into sandstone) and bed boundaries. These erosive forces have created the fusion of corrie and crag which can be seen in superabun-dance on this enchanting walk.

Another important feature of the crags of many Torridonian mountains, and especially the corrie crags seen on this walk, is the deeply etched gullies running in more or less straight lines down through the beds. One of the most impressive of such gullies is to be seen on the next corrie, but many others can be seen on the crags of Coire na Feola. Each gully is matched by a small debris cone or fan at its base. The blocks of rock and smaller lumps that are broken off the crags by freeze-thaw, physical erosion (for example as large lumps crash down the gully they bash other bits off the rocks) and chemical erosion are moved down by gravity to collect at the base. Many gullies will start their existence on sites of some weakness in the rocks, such as a fault or joint.

Coire na Feola (Photo w7.1) is significantly more impressive than the fairly shallow Coire Each. It cuts back into the mountain mass for almost 1km from its lip to the top of the 200m-high backwall. There is a small, inner corrie right at the back with a small waterfall draining it. This would probably have held a small glacier at the very end of the ice age after the much bigger glacier in the main corrie had melted.

It is necessary to lose some height to get round the separating buttress into the next corrie, Coire na Poite. The further down you drop the easier the terrain – you may want to drop all the way to Lochan Coire na Poite which is carved into a flat area outside the corrie.

You also get a preview of the fourth corrie, Coire an Fhamair, as you drop down before re-ascending into Coire na Poite. However, your attention will probably be drawn to the rounded end of the buttress dividing Coire na Poite and Coire an Fhamair. From some angles, this circular buttress looks rather like some dreary modern office block with darkened windows. In fact, as you go further into the corrie it can be seen that the buttress is separated from the main spur by a particularly deep gully.

Make your way up into Coire na Poite. This is probably the most impressive of all the corries to be seen on the recommended walk, both from below and later on looking down from the summit ridge. The crags are as much as 350m high in places, creating the impression of being inside a massive amphitheatre.

There are two small lochans within the upper corrie that are out of sight from lower down. To reach the upper corrie, make your way up grass patches between rock outcrops on the rock bar holding in the two lochans. Once within the inner corrie, the experience of the surrounding crags is almost overwhelming.

You have to drop down again to get out of the inner corrie and round into Coire an Fhamair, making your way below the rounded buttress. Being broader and less craggy, Coire an Fhamair is much less claustrophobic than the Coire na Poite. There is much scree to the right and the back, although the southern crags are very impressive.

Beinn Bhan

Photo w7.2 | Glacial and periglacial (freeze-thaw) erosion created these remnants of crags in Coire na Poite.

It is a hard slog up from the bottom of the corrie to reach the summit ridge at its lowest point, with some 300m of ascent. The steep slope will however encourage you to take frequent stops for a breather, providing the opportunity to turn away from the oppressive slope and look outwards to the widening view to the east. This also gives you very impressive views of the massive crags on the south side of the corrie. Interestingly, the rounded, largely separated buttress is less conspicuous from this angle and appears just as part of the overall crag with its vertical gullies cut into its face.

As you ascend you will notice two large rock outcrops on the right. They look initially as if they might be the remnants of a landslide, but as you pass them it becomes evident that they are isolated tors or towers that used to be part of a spur from the main crags. In essence, they are substantially eroded versions of the large, rounded, partially separated buttress seen in Coire na Poite (see Photo w7.2).

The two tors are surrounded by big blocks that have fallen off them and also by a collection of blocks and scree that has fallen from higher up and then collected behind the two tors. These mounds of fallen blocks give you a feel for the process of freeze-thaw which was responsible for widening the joints and gullies cut into the rock, eventually isolating parts of a spur and breaking off over steepened parts of the crags.

At some point you will no doubt resort to zigzaging to minimise the effort of climbing the last steepish part of the corrie backwall. All the pain will be forgotten as soon as you reach

Photo w7.3 | Highly eroded Torridonian sandstone forms a low, layered, smooth
rounded hill with erosion working on the conspicuous bedding planes.

the ridge and enjoy the sudden appearance of wonderful views to the west. (Watch out on
windy days for strong westerlies hitting you as you reach the ridge.)

On reaching the summit ridge, the direct return route is to bear left (south). However, if
you have time and energy don't miss out the chance to overlook one more corrie, Coire Toll
a' Mheine about 250m to the north. Follow the edge of the ridge overlooking at first Coire an
Fhamair, then bear north along the edge to where it turns left above Coire Toll a' Mheine. The
views of Loch Lundie and the mountains beyond are well worth this short diversion.

Don't overlook the less conspicuous intervening hills to the east: An Staonach
(NG 830 480) lies behind Loch Gaineamhach, Loch Dubh and a handful of smaller lochans.
These low hills illustrate a much greater stage of erosion of a mountain made of Torridonian
sandstone, providing a slightly different version of ancient gneiss 'knock and lochan' topography. In this case, the 'knock' is layered and smooth sandstone, its rounded shape reflecting
its geological difference from knobbly gneiss knocks (see Photo w7.3).

Looking further to the east towards Sgurr a' Gharaidh, the geological interest switches
to two features – the presence of a big chunk of limestone and of thrust zones created by the
collision of continental tectonic plates (see Photo w7.4).

Fairly small areas of limestone (dating back to just over 500 million years ago) can be
found down the boundary between the ancient gneiss and Torridonian sandstone to the north
and west and the younger Cambrian rocks to the south and east. One of the best-known

Beinn Bhan

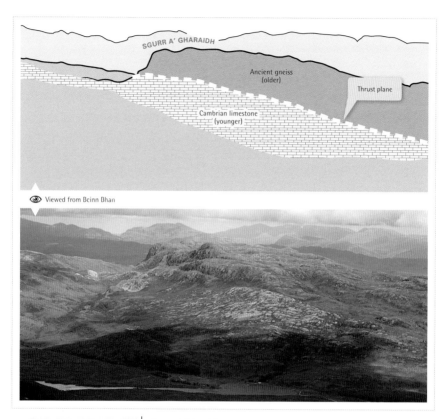

Photo w7.4 + Diagram w7.1 | Sgurr a' Gharaidh.

limestone areas is in Assynt (see Walk 4). Between Assynt and Applecross the limestone is restricted except for one small wider area just north of Ullapool. Another limited exposure of the limestone is found on the western flanks of Sgurr a' Gharaidh.

Lying on top of the 550 million year old Cambrian limestone is a mass of approximately 3 billion year old gneiss. These ancient rocks were thrust up on top of the younger rocks by the gargantuan forces generated by the collision of continental tectonic plates.

In fact, the limestone has also been thrust on top of a thin layer of younger Cambrian quartzites which form the base of the western flank of Sgurr a' Gharaidh. The area to the northeast of Sgurr a' Gharaidh (along the line of hills An Ruadh stac, Maol Chean-dearg, Sgurr Dubh and onto Beinn Eighe) has several of these thrust lines, leaving a complex mix of Cambrian quartzite, Torridonian sandstone and thin streaks of ancient gneiss.

When you've fully enjoyed the views, make your way back towards the summit of the ridge. The most dramatic views are had by keeping fairly close to the edge above the corries. Take great care when you peer over the edge of the crags at the top of Coire na Poite shortly before reaching the summit for the most dramatic view of the day (see Photo w7.5). The rock bar holding in the left-hand lochan is quite clearly seen.

Photo w7.5

Coire na Poite seen

from above.

Continue along the summit ridge to the southeast (again keeping as close to the edge as feels prudent) for views of the crags and lochans of Coire na Poite and the arête separating it from Coire na Feola, A' Chioch.

The ridge thins for a short section above Coire na Feola, but it is not frightfully narrow and should pose no real problems as long as it is walked with care. The biggest danger will be the magical views of Skye and the coast, as well as the nearby mountains in every direction, distracting you from where you are putting your feet.

After passing the top of Coire Each, the ridge starts to lose its sharp shape and it is necessary to pick a route back down to the road. The terrain can be awkward when wet. Traces of track come and go on the descent, but pick your point of approach to the road and keep it in view as you move about to find the easiest route through the small crags and boggy patches. Remember to avoid the quarry by aiming either to its left or right as you near the road.

Beinn Bhan

Photo w7.6 | Coire a' Chaorachain seen from Beinn Bhan.

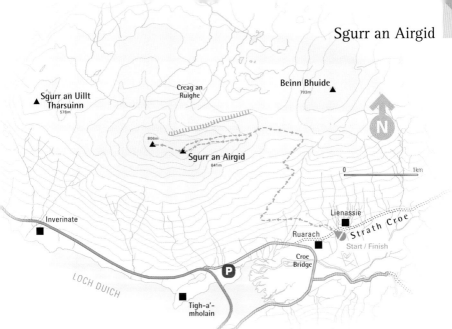

Walk #8

Sgurr an Airgid

START	▶	NG 960 210
FINISH	●	NG 960 210
TIME	⏱	4 HOURS+
GRADE	🧭	NAVIGATION ● ● ●
	⛰	TERRAIN ● ● ●
	⚡	SEVERITY ● ● ●

Sgurr an Airgid occupies a strategic viewpoint above one of the most scenic valleys of the Highlands, standing as it does just to the northeast of Glen Shiel and the Five Sisters of Kintail. As befits such a well-placed hill, the views from the summit are outstanding.

The hill is mainly formed of metamorphic Moine rocks and there is plenty of shiny schist to be seen on the walk. There is a considerable variety of the Moine

Sgurr an Airgid

rocks and not all are shiny. It is also worth noting that the shine is dampened by dull weather and by weathering of the rocks, and it sometimes takes an effort to spot the shine on well-weathered rocks on dull days. Freshly exposed rocks such as pebbles are often better for seeing the shiny crystals.

Ancient gneiss also features marginally in the area thanks to a thrust zone which brings these fairly old rocks to the surface. The ancient gneiss was originally formed as igneous rocks, but the Moine rocks were first laid down as sedimentary material. The metamorphosis in both cases took place during the collision of continental plates (though at vastly different times) when the crustal rocks were subjected to high temperatures and pressures. This led to recrystallisation of the minerals within the rocks, but without their melting (see Chapter 6). It also led to deformation of the recrystallising minerals, forming convoluted shapes in the rocks (see Chapter 7). These features are seen in abundance on this walk.

The scenery is utterly magnificent throughout the walk, giving outstanding views of the post-glacial landscape. This whole area has been deeply eroded by massive ice sheets that covered the entire region, riding over the hills. The signs of glacial scouring of the upland plateau, such as on Sgurr an Airgid itself, and of deep 'valley glaciers' that have carved the superb U-shaped valleys are all around.

Head west along the minor road from the car park for a short distance, then turn right at the T-junction and then right again at the next junction. Follow the track and turn left (north) immediately after an industrial unit. Pass through two gates to follow a broad vehicle track, which fizzles out after 100m or so. Carry on in roughly the same direction, but rise up a bit to see a small marker post and narrow track up on the right.

Shiny schist can be seen in pebbles as soon as you pass the industrial unit, giving a feel for the main rock type to be seen on this walk. The pebbles are not all similar, however. There are shiny ones and lineated ones, some shiny and lineated, some shiny, lineated and deformed. They are variously light grey, grey and almost black in colour. Higher up the hill, some display reddish and whitish crystals. Some of the rocks also have highly distinctive lichen on them.

Follow the narrow track up until it suddenly debouches you onto another broad vehicle track. Note this point well, as it is easy to miss on the way down. Turn right and follow the track uphill, enjoying the increasingly attractive views. This vehicle track also peters out and a muddy track leads to a gate – watch the top of your head if you are tall as you pass through!

The track then heads towards a stream, continues up towards the south-western flanks of Beinn Bhuide and eventually brings you out onto the eastern side of the bealach (col) between Beinn Bhuide and Sgurr an Airgid. If you have the time and energy, a short diversion to the summit of Beinn Bhuide is worth the small amount of additional ascent.

Otherwise, head north of west to cross the bealach. Although the centre of the bealach is impassable with peaty mud and peat hags, it can easily be passed on either the north or south side. My recommendation for the ascent is to head to the northern side and find a way past the peat. There are some highly impressive outcrops of the schist on display in this area, showing quite severe deformation in places (see Photo w8.1).

Once past the peaty area, identify the track ascending towards the summit (to the right of rock outcrops on the southern edge) and trudge up to the first top (a false summit). It is worth spending a little time enjoying the views from the false summit before heading to the true summit and its trig point for more views.

For the very best views, however, go beyond the summit and cross some 300m to the west (about 100m west of the spot height 806m on the OS 1:50,000 map; the western summit is actually just over 820m high). The rock outcrops provide plenty of opportunities to sit comfortably out of any wind.

Photo w8.1 | Deformation of Moine metamorphic rocks.

Photo w8.2 | Gleann Lichd, a classic steep-sided glacial valley.

Sgurr an Airgid

Here there are utterly magnificent views of Skye and other islands, Knoydart, the Saddle, Applecross, Beinn Bhan and even Beinn Eighe. Beinn Bhan looks rather like a couple of waves that have been frozen in time, an effect created by the green, smooth slopes of the west-facing flanks of the hill and the corresponding chunks bitten out of the hill by ice on the east.

You can see the tilt of the rocks on the nearest hill to you to the north, Carn Bad a'Chreamha, at NG 925 264. The terrain is much rougher beyond that hill, with lots of heather rather than the firm grassy terrain of Sgurr an Airgid. Anyone who has followed the walks in this book in order will have noticed the difference between the effort required for the earlier walks and this one. The rough terrain beyond Carn Bad a'Chreamha is due to ancient gnarly gneiss reaching the surface on that section of the hillside.

The same outcrop actually throws a narrow seam across the shallow bealach which you crossed to get to the spot between Sgurr an Airgid's true summit and the western viewpoint. We will take a look at some of the gneiss on the return journey, which begins when you are able to tear yourself away from the ravishing views.

Head back across the summit plateau, checking out the various outcrops. In some you will see pinkish granitic layers within the outcrops of ancient gneiss (see Photo w8.3). The band of gneiss which crosses the bealach is actually split into two parts by a fault which runs east–west along the bealach, so that the southern stretch of the gneiss is about 100m to the east of the northern stretch.

Cross over to the northern side of the bealach for more interesting rocks and views of the north- and northeast-facing corries running away from the summit ridge. Among the rocks are some examples of severe distortion (see Photo w8.4) and of the way in which weathering attacks the weaknesses represented by lineation within the rocks (see Photo w8.5).

Photo w8.3 | Granite and gneiss exposed on the summit plateau of Sgurr an Airgid.

Photo w8.4 | Deformation folds.

Photo w8.5 | Erosion along lineation in the rocks.

For the descent there are two choices. The more adventurous is to pick a route along the splitting fingers of outcrops on the right (south). There are occasional traces of track, but most of the time there is no track to follow. Trial and error will be necessary to find a through route as the various fingers come to an end, and you will need to move around to find a feasible route. Those who revel in rock will stay with the rock outcrops all the way to the lower bealach, enjoying largely easy scrambling. The more prudent will prefer to head back to the track used for the ascent from the bealach.

This time keep on the southern edge of the bealach for fine views across to Beinn Fhada, the northern peaks of the Five Sisters, the Saddle and Knoydart (see Photo w8.6). If you look carefully, you can see the way all the rocks of these hills tilt from lower left to upper right. This is large-scale deformation caused by collision of continental tectonic plates. The smaller-scale deformation seen on the rocks on this walk took place within the larger deformation zone. This 'plastic' deformation and metamorphism occur fairly low in the earth's crust, so these rocks spent a lot of time deep down before being raised near the surface and exposed by erosion of the overlying rocks.

Photo w8.6 | View towards Loch Dubh and the Glen Shiel mountains.

Sgurr an Airgid

Return to the cairn at the top of track that leads back to the start point, appreciating the views as you go. Lower down, remember to keep an eye out for the inconspicuous track that leaves the vehicle track to the left. If you pass a large rock outcrop on the right and then a dug-out area on the left while on that vehicle track, you have gone too far and need to go back 30–40m. Having located the track, follow it back down to the start point.

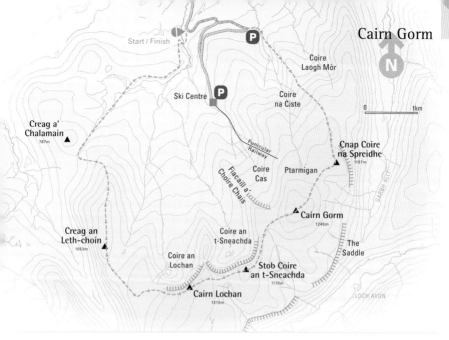

Walk #9

Cairn Gorm

START	▶	NH 985 073
FINISH	●	NH 985 073
TIME	🕒	6 HOURS+
GRADE	🧭	NAVIGATION ● ● ●
	☁	TERRAIN ● ● ●
	⊗	SEVERITY ● ● ● ● ●

A glance at a geological map of the Cairngorms gives the impression that there is little variation in the geology. The Cairngorms are a mass of granite, formed from molten magma created when a lower part of the continental tectonic plate was heated beyond its melting point. The magma rose up a short way before cooling slowly to produce the large crystals of quartz and other minerals (feldspar and mica) which define 'granite'.

Cairn Gorm

The result is the rolling landscape, whose only features in this otherwise undistinguished scene are the grand corries and trenches carved by the ice age. The geology map shows all of this as a simple red blob, with very few if any faults or features.

As this walk will demonstrate however, there is actually a much more complex geological story to tell than that revealed by the standard geological map. The geological history of the Cairngorm Granite is outlined in Chapter 8, and it is well worth reading that chapter in conjunction with the walk description.

Cairn Gorm is the second-highest point in the Cairngorms and is situated at the heart of one of its wildest mountain regions. Great open skies rise above a stark rolling plateau which in places is cut into by spectacular corries and glacial trenches.

Cairn Gorm is a mountain of contrasts. This great 'wilderness', by far the largest upland plateau above 900m in Britain, is also one of the most highly spoiled of the Scottish Highlands landscapes. The result is the extensive paraphernalia of ski runs, a funicular railway, several buildings on several sites, a prominent servicing track which goes up to the upper station and a couple of extensive high-level car parks.

The contrasts also apply to practical matters. Walks in the Cairngorms can be very long, and one guidebook offers a selection of strolls of 22km with 1600m of ascent. Cairn Gorm is however an extremely easy mountain to climb. This is not because of the funicular railway which can transport large groups to about 165m below the summit. In fact, those using the railway are actually not allowed to leave the station premises for 'conservation' reasons – unless they pay a fee to be led on a walk.

Rather, it is the high-level car parks (the upper one at 630m) which can significantly reduce the amount of ascent needed to reach the summit. The higher car park is also served by bus. There are several quite easy routes onto the north Cairngorms plateau, with long easy-angled ridges making the task a fairly easy one. The recommended walk uses a medium-level car park as a start and finish point, using the ridges to take a look at the contrasting landscape features of Cairn Gorm and the northern corries. A glimpse of the great glacial trench of Lairig Ghru is included.

The views once you reach the ridge are wonderful and on a warm, sunny day this is an enticing landscape. Under such conditions it is hard to imagine that this can also be a viciously harsh place. Wind is the biggest danger to the walker, whether on its own or whipping rain, hail or snow into fiercely propelled pellets. The weather can change from benign to evil in minutes, another of the contrasts of the Cairngorms.

The wide spaces, even on the recommended walk which largely follows ridges, make for challenging navigation in the mist. Indeed, the very scale of the mountain may make for difficult navigation even in good weather.

For this reason, it is worth thinking about routes of retreat in case you decide that withdrawal is better than ploughing on in unfavourable conditions, and there are several good 'escape' routes off the ridge. The easiest way is probably from the summit of Cairn Gorm itself – the route from the summit to the Ptarmigan restaurant/railway station complex is densely cairned and there is a wide vehicle track which drops down to the upper car park. I have to add that I have never used this section of the route and would never want to. I would not hesitate to use it in case of necessity, however.

I have used the following three tracks and can recommend them all as escape routes or to cut the recommended walk short. There are two good tracks that, once found, are easy to follow and can take you all the way back from the main ridge to the upper or middle car parks. One descends north along Fiacaill a' Choire Chais (starting from spot height 1141 at about NH 999 039, 600m west of the summit of Cairn Gorm), eventually becoming entangled with the skiing infrastructure near the upper car park. The other is the path from/to Ben Macdui which runs north–south along the ridge from Miadan Creag an Leth-choin. The track is not visible in the mist from spot height 1083 (at about NH 9752 0242), and is about 150m east of the cairn. Finding the track could be difficult in misty conditions, but once found it should be easy to follow.

These ridge routes may not be suitable in fierce winds or lightning, so a useful escape route is via Coire an t-Sneachda. A handy track starts from the bealach between Cairn Lochan and Stob Coire an t-Sneachda at about NH 9910 0275. After an initial short but steep scramble (which may not suit everyone) down about 200m to the collection of tiny lochans and boulders, the walk back to the car park is pretty straightforward.

This route is probably the quickest (with the exception of the Cairn Gorm vehicle track) and offers a highly attractive way on to or off of the main ridge. It could be used as an alternative start route, cutting out some of the recommended walk and making use of a higher car park – at the expense of views of the small but fascinating Chalamain Gap and the large and truly spectacular Lairig Ghru. Alternatively, you could use this route to cut the recommended walk into two smaller circular walks.

Cairn Gorm

Pick a nice day and all these warnings will seem utterly superfluous as you waltz happily around the full recommended walk. Chance upon a day when vile weather closes in, however, and you will be relieved to have noted the possible escape routes.

Start from the car park where the road does a sharp U-bend near the upper reaches of Glen More Forest. Cross the road in the axis of the bend to pick up a footpath which drops down to a bridge across the burn Allt Creag an Leth-choin at about NH 9255 0753. Cross the bridge and follow the track as it runs along the edge of the V-shaped valley. The track eventually crosses the stream again (at about NH 974 062) and heads up towards the obvious feature of the Chalamain Gap. Another similar unnamed gap can be seen in early parts of the walk just south of Airgiod-meall at around NH 965 065.

Both these 'gaps' are glacial meltwater channels (see Chapter 11) and form the upper limbs of a Y-shaped valley (albeit at different heights of 570m and 700m, the Chalamain Gap being the higher).

Photo w9.1 | Looking back towards the start of the walk through the Chalamain Gap. Note jointing in outcrops on the side which have been deepened by freeze-thaw action, breaking the rock up into blocks which form the blocky scree.

As you reach the Chalamain Gap the way becomes narrower and rockier, especially as it nears the highest point (see Photo w9.1). Despite the difficulty in crossing the boulders, it doesn't take long to pass the 250m of the length of the gap. The structure of the gap is worth noting with plenty of rock falls and some impressive crags (see Photos w9.1 and 8.4).

The jointing of the granite is very well displayed. These are developed from very ancient cooling joints formed when the granite was injected up from below as molten rock and began to cool very slowly. The hot magma also heated up water which carried minerals into the microscopic joints, chemically altering the granite around it. Such 'thermally altered' zones are more susceptible to erosion than areas unaffected by jointing and thermal fluids.

It therefore seems likely that the gap is sited on a weak zone in the rock which was exploited by high-pressure glacial meltwaters during the recent ice age, carving out this channel. Those parts of the Cairngorm granite which were most affected by jointing are often those associated with present-day low points such as valleys and bealachs (see Chapter 8).

Pass right through the gap far enough to get a view of the bowl shape in the mountainside heading down into the northern reaches of the Lairig Ghru. As soon as the slope relents, head roughly southeast onto the ridge and then head south up the ridge to Creag an Lethchoin (Lurcher's Crag). The route takes you through plenty of outcrops and boulders of granite, some pinkish and some nearly all grey in colour (see Photos 8.2 and 8.3). The pinkish-tinged rocks come from areas with more jointing and which therefore underwent more chemical alteration (due to the presence of hot fluids in the rock shortly after it was formed).

Photo w9.2 | The great glacial breaching point and trench of the Lairig Ghru, one of the key scenic features of the Cairngorms, is sited on a zone of 'thermally altered' rock which created a weakness subsequently exploited by glaciers.

The slope is gentle and you soon arrive at the sub-summit at height 1026m (NH 969 039). Continue towards the higher summit point at 1053m (NH 968 033). Head a few metres west of the summit to overlook the Lairig Ghru, the deeply etched glacial trench which cuts right through the Cairngorms (see Photo w9.2).

The Lairig Ghru is one of the major scenic and structural features of the Cairngorms, and is located along a thermally altered zone which has weakened the rock's resistance to erosion. Glaciers then carved the glacial trench along the line of this weakness. The high point seen in Photo w9.2 is a glacial breaching point where glaciers from the north rode up over the mountain to flow into the southern end of the glacial valley. Lairig Ghru is the only major glacial breaching point in the Cairngorms massif.

Head initially south along the edge of the valley top, then aim roughly southeast towards

Cairn Gorm

spot height 1083m (at about NH 9752 0242). From there, head roughly east to the slopes of Cairn Lochan before climbing up to its summit point at 1215m. Stick as close to the edge of the corrie backwall as is prudent for fantastic views of the crags running down into Coire an Lochain. From a few places you can get a glimpse of the 'Great Slab', where a large section of granite has broken off along a continuous joint surface.

From Cairn Lochan to the other side of Stob Coire an t-Sneachda you are presented with superb views of the corries and of the granite exposed in the corrie backwalls. The varied jointing of the granite – horizontal and vertical, straight and curved – can also be observed. This is a key internal feature of the granite, as more jointing means more erosion.

The joints allow freeze-thaw action to break up the exposed rock. Piles of boulders created by weathering and freeze-thaw in crags, ready to fall down and add to the confusion of boulders in the corrie below, lie all around (see Photos w9.3 and 8.5).

Photo w9.3 | Jointing in the backwall of Stob Coire an t-Sneachda, with isolated pillars getting ready to topple. The small dark shape centre-left is a lateral moraine left by a glacier flowing out of the corrie.

While areas with lots of jointing are more easily eroded, those areas with less jointing tend to stand proud. This is the key to another feature of the Cairngorm granite: rock tors. These isolated clumps of rock – up to 10m in height – appear in some places but not others. The 'Barns of Bynack' and the tors of Beinn Meadhoin are visible from this walk (see Photo w9.6), and a remnant tor is visited after the summit of Cairn Gorm (see Photo w9.5).

Take a close look into Coire an t-Sneachda as you descend from Cairn Lochan and then go up and down over Stob Coire an t-Sneachda (see Photo w9.4). Tucked up under the crags you can see the lochans where once there was the seat of a glacier. You can also see the mass of boulders littering the area around the lochans, and the way the mass is shaped into moraines.

A ridge twists along the right side of the corrie (it is easily seen by the shadow it casts in Photo w9.4). This may be a moraine, perhaps having held a glacier between the ridge and the hillside or as a lateral moraine on the side of a glacier in the centre of the valley. Alternatively, it may be another feature referred to as the impressive-sounding 'protalus rampart'. Such a feature is thought to be created by rocks falling down the mountainside, sliding over ice at the base of the slope and collecting as a linear mound parallel to the slope. The break in the mound seen in the photo may have been caused by erosion and the mound may once have been continuous.

Photo w9.4 | Moraines in Coire an t-Sneachda. The most conspicuous is a lateral moraine on the centre right, but recessional moraines are also visible in the centre and lower centre.

Photo w9.5 | Well-eroded tor near the summit of Cairn Gorm.

From the top of the backwall of Coire an t-Sneachda it is necessary to lose about 70m of height and then to ascend a further 145m to the summit of Cairn Gorm where you encounter a radio transmitter, a well-cairned track pointing down to the restaurant and (quite likely) a crowd of other visitors. Views from the summit itself are somewhat limited, being in the middle of a flattish plateau.

Cairn Gorm

Photo w9.6 | View towards Loch Avon from near the summit of Cairn Gorm.

Head to the conspicuous tor about 150m east of the summit (see Photo w9.5), the only substantial feature on the summit plateau apart from the boulder field. This well-eroded tor is not as high as some of the others in the Cairngorms, but it gives a good feel of what a tor looks like. The tor provides much more expansive views than the summit point (see Photo w9.6) and also somewhere to sit out of the wind if necessary (which it usually is).

If you prefer to call it a day on Cairn Gorm, rather than go down via the restaurant track return to the col on the western side and descend the ridge from spot height 1131 at NJ 998 039. To continue with the full route, head for Cnap Coire na Spreidhe. Walk towards the conspicuous outcrops at the northern end of the long loop in the 1000m contour (at about NH 0125 0545), enjoying the views east with the Barns of Bynack easily seen on the skyline.

Pass an area of fascinating outcrops as you descend west of north to meet a clear track coming through Coire na Ciste, eventually joining it at about NH 0065 0635. Follow the path to the car park at NH 998 074 and then follow the tarmac road back to the start point.

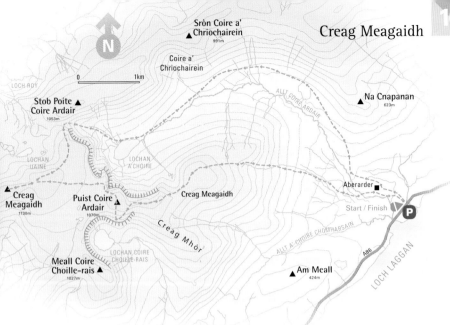

Walk #10

Creag Meagaidh

START	▶	NN 483 872
FINISH	●	NN 483 872
TIME	⏱	5 HOURS+
GRADE	⬆	NAVIGATION ● ● ●
	⛰	TERRAIN ● ● ● ●
	✳	SEVERITY ● ● ● ●

Creag Meagaidh is a very popular mountain and is part of a wider plateau range, with wide views and superb high-level walking. The recommended route is a very varied one, starting with a fine walk through an atmospheric glacial valley and corrie, an ascent to an unusual feature known as 'The Window', a walk on the wide open plateau, a loop around the top of two glacial corries and finally a fairly straightforward descent.

Creag Meagaidh

The key points of geological interest are the sharply angled dip of the rocks, a craggy glacial corrie with a lochan, 'The Window' (actually a glacial meltwater channel), the wide open views of the surrounding landscape, views of glacial 'parallel roads', an intrusive granite dyke and the overview of two corries and their crags.

The rocks are all metamorphic and part of the Grampian Group, mainly schists. The area is also affected by intrusions of granite, some of it a very coarse type of granite known as pegmatite. A clear granite intrusion is crossed on the return leg of the journey.

Creag Meagaidh is part of a nature reserve from which grazing animals have been removed. The result is that a vast variety of vegetation, and especially trees, now manages to survive and prosper in the lower areas. The full effects of the present land management policy will only be seen in the future, but already it is clear to even the casual observer that there is considerable biodiversity and much more interesting surrounds.

The presence of the nature reserve means that there is a large car park at the start/finish point, 'interpretation' information and several signed trails, on which the recommended walk begins and ends. It is only for the first (and last) five minutes or so that you follow the signed trails before you make your way along a good track into the wild valley of Coill a' Choire, climbing steadily and gently towards Coire Ardair and The Window.

From the car park follow the 'red' signed route, but leave it for an unmarked path on the right where the signed route swings left. The unmarked path appears to be taking you towards the hill on the right, Na Cnapanan, but does in fact direct you into Coill a' Choire. As you pass through part of an established plantation, the views into the valley begin to open up.

The 'immature' glacial corrie of Coire a' Chriochairein can be seen high on the right-hand side (north) of the valley. You can also see landslips in superficial material cut by the river on the left (south) and plenty of hummocky moraines in the valley floor.

The Window comes into view after a short while, followed by the main crags of Coire Ardair. When the path moves down towards the river, hummocky moraines are well displayed.

The walk rises slowly until suddenly Lochan a' Choire comes into view, adding great beauty to the craggy architecture of the corrie backwall (see Photo w10.1). The crags are clearly broken by a series of lines running from upper left to lower right. These form significant diagonal 'steps' which shape the face of the crags, as will become more apparent as you ascend towards The Window after passing the lochan. There are more or less well-vegetated debris cones at the base of each step. All the rocks which fall off the crags above each step are guided down by the sloping step into the piled rocks forming the cones.

Photo w10.1 | Lochan a' Choire, the crags of Coire Ardair and (right) The Window.

The diagonal lines show the major tilt of these rocks, forming part of a major 'antiform' which extends across Loch Laggan and the valley over to the mountains in the south. There is a corresponding 'synform' to the north and west of the Creag Meagaidh plateau, although there is also a large granite intrusion on that side of the plateau which complicates the situation. The whole Grampian mountain range has been badly deformed into antiforms and synforms. Where un-metamorphosed rocks are folded they form 'anticlines' and 'synclines'; the terms antiform and synform are however employed when discussing metamorphic folds, to indicate that they are not distortions of the original bedding lines, but of the lineations created during metamorphism as similar minerals congregate into layers.

Once past the loch, start the long ascent towards The Window. The final parts of the ascent are not overly steep, but the loose scree is a bit slithery. Remember to stop and turn round to look at the diagonal 'steps' in the crags (see Photo w10.2). From this angle, it is clear that the fearsome-looking crags seen on the approach are far from forming a continuous near-vertical backwall to the corrie. Instead, the tilted stratification has led to a stepped set of crags, each forming its own mini-corrie wall. The return leg of the recommended route takes you past the top of the steps.

Creag Meagaidh

Photo w10.2 | Tilted rocks forming the crags above Lochan a' Choire.

Photo w10.3 | 'The Window': a glacial meltwater channel cut through the plateau.

Further up on the climb to The Window, take the opportunity to turn around and have a high-level look down at the lochan and the southern arm of the valley. A small glacial corrie can be seen with a stream running out of it down to join the outlet of Lochan a' Choire. Note the considerable amount of scree cloaking the lower parts of the crags on either side, much of which is now covered by vegetation.

Carry on up to The Window. It looks like a small high-level col from below but, on arrival at its level of 940m, it suddenly transforms into a gently tilting and narrow rocky valley (see Photo w10.3). A similar feature is met on Walk 9 in the Cairngorms (Chalamain Gap), although situated at the somewhat lower level of 700m.

The Window and the Chalamain gap are both glacial meltwater channels. They were created by powerful streams quite possibly running underneath glaciers under great pressure, or when large quantities of dammed water were suddenly released. Go right through the meltwater channel to see a sort of bowl around its northern end, below which there is a step to lower ground and the rolling plateau of the Monadhliath beyond.

From beyond the channel, bear left (south) to find an easily angled path to the summit plateau. Remember to turn around before you gain too much height, so that you can appreciate The Window as a narrow gash through the plateau which stretches from the summit area of Creag Meagaidh to Stob Poite Coire Ardair and several other tops beyond.

As you ascend, pick up a track running along the northern edge of the summit plateau. The track takes you to a large cairn on the northern edge of the widest part of the summit plateau – this is not the summit, however. It is situated a further 500m to the west at NN 418 875, where the plateau narrows to a wide neck.

Enjoy the panoramic views which extend to the west to Ben Nevis, the Aonachs and the Grey Corries. To the north the hills are more subdued with rolling uplands separated by wide boggy-looking lower ground, although there are hints of sharper peaks beyond. It is worth approaching the edges of the summit ridge to the north and south of the cairn to enjoy the views.

One interesting feature is the trace of the 'parallel roads' (see Chapter 11 and Walk 11) which record the levels of glacial lakes at the north-eastern extension of the top of Glen Roy. To the northwest, note the upper two parallel roads (at 325m and 350m) on the northern side of the valley, on the southern flanks of Carn Dearg Beag (NN 365 941). The 'roads' disappear from view, hidden by the intervening heights. In fact, the 350m road extends a lot further on the hidden southern side of the valley (almost to due north of the summit cairn of Creag Meagaidh) as a recognisable feature on the ground.

With the glacial meltwater channel of The Window and traces of the parallel roads, it is clear that the ice age had a complex effect on this whole area and that not all features of the ice age are directly attributable to frozen water. Vast quantities of meltwater were released as the glaciers melted, often with dramatic effect.

From the summit aim just north of east until you rejoin the wide summit plateau area, then head just south of east to meet the top of the crags above Coire Ardair. This is not as easy a task as it sounds. The sloping 'steps' in the crags (noted earlier) mean that there is no single top to the backwall of the corrie.

Navigation across the plateau requires care in clear conditions, and may be very difficult in mist because of the uncertain nature of the Coire Ardair backwall. In clear weather, head towards the visible rising ground of Puist Coire Ardair (NN 436 873) but aim left towards the top of the crags as you near the apparent top of the Coire Ardair crags. You will not want to go right to the edge of the crags, but aim right to cross a boggy area in the dip between the Creag Meagaidh summit plateau and Puist Coire Ardair. Climb roughly east to the prominent nose beyond the dip. The views from the higher point down into Coire Ardair are spectacular.

Then aim south to cross the plateau to meet the top of the crags above Coire Choille-rais to get a view down into this corrie. Although the corrie is on the southern flank, it has carved an eastern aspect. The lochan and its impressive enclosing crags are classic corrie shape with a rock bar holding in the loch (see Photo w10.4). Observe the clear dip of the rock stratification from upper left to lower right, part of the same large 'antiform' that we saw on the way through Coire Ardair.

Creag Meagaidh

Photo w10.4 | A classic glacial corrie, Coire Choille-rais with steeply dipping rocks in the backwall.

When you have appreciated the views of Coire Choille-rais and the mountain landscape beyond, aim once again for the summit of Puist Coire Ardair before heading east, following the northern edge of the crags above Coire Ardair. The stepped nature of the corrie crags is quite evident and you can walk out to various prominences along the way (some requiring care) for fantastic views of the corrie and, from some viewpoints, of the sloping rock stratification in the crags of Coire Ardair and of The Window. Take especial care as you approach the second cairn on Puist Coire Ardair in mist or high wind, as there is a big vertical drop just a footstep or two beyond the cairn. You get a good view along this section of the unnamed glacial corrie and its tiny lochan nestling in the valley side a short distance ahead of you and to the left (north).

Drop down slightly to a shallow bealach where you cross an area of reddish-tinged rocks. This is a granite intrusion which crosses the ridge and dips down towards Lochan a' Choire. Continue along the ridge to spot height 1001m (NN 4484 8777) on Sron a' Ghoire. Enjoy the last views of Coire Ardair and then start descending from the summit, passing a set of strange, small valleys with some tiny lochans on the way. Head roughly just north of east towards the head of the burn, Allt Bealach a' Ghoire.

Your objective (a bridge at NN 4756 8474) is not directly in sight as it is hidden by trees (and is not shown on the OS map). However, a large boulder (at NN 4759 8744) is visible from quite a way up and makes a useful spot to aim for (although a direct route is not practicable). Traces of track appear and disappear as you pick a route down close to Allt Bealach a' Ghoire, but you have to move around to find the easiest ground. The track becomes clearer lower down before crossing hummocky moraines, dropping steeply off the final hummock. The large boulder is gone from view for a time, but by then you should have been able to get onto a fairly well-defined track. Cross the very substantial bridge and then follow signs back to the start point.

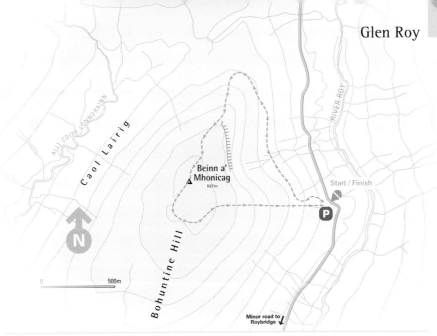

Walk #11

Glen Roy

START	▶	NN 297 852
FINISH	●	NN 297 852
TIME	🕒	1 HOUR+
GRADE	⊕	NAVIGATION ● ●
	◔	TERRAIN ● ●
	⊗	SEVERITY ● ●

One of the most famous of Scotland's geological sites is Glen Roy with its 'parallel roads'. The 'roads' are not confined to Glen Roy, but can also be seen in Glen Gloy and its subsidiary valley, Glen Fintaig. The same feature can also be traced on both sides of Glen Spean from under Aonach Mor all the way east to the subsidiary valley of Coire Laire under the Grey Corries, but is less conspicuous (often hidden by plantation

Glen Roy

forest). The 'roads' resolutely follow the contours, even into the smallest side valley.

The parallel roads certainly give the impression of being human-made structures, running horizontally for significant distances. Indeed, part of one of the parallel roads on the southern side of Glen Spean was used for a (now dismantled) tramway, built during the construction of a hydroelectric scheme to power an aluminium works (whose pipelines can be seen from north of Fort William on the northern flank of Ben Nevis).

In the 1860s a Swiss geologist Louis Agassiz, who was familiar with glacial features in the Alps, recognised the 'roads' as the stranded former shores of great glacial lakes dammed up behind glaciers.

The lake(s) existed for a few hundred years about 12,500 years ago. At this time the bulk of Glen Roy was free of glaciers; however, a large glacier did exist in the Great Glen. As temperatures fell, this glacier pushed lobes up into Glen Gloy, Glen Spean and Glen Roy. During summer months, meltwater coming off the mountains around these glens could flow into the valleys but could not flow out because of the glacier lobes lower down in the glens which formed ice dams. Instead, the meltwater collected behind the glacier lobes forming large lakes.

When a lake existed, it left a layer of deposits at the lake edge. As there are three 'roads' (at approximately 260, 325 and 350m), it is assumed that the lake went through two successive reductions in height before it disappeared completely when the ice melted.

The trip up into Glen Roy to see this impressive sight is well worth the 5km drive up to a parking place and viewpoint. For the best views, it is of course necessary to put on boots and take to your feet.

The recommended route offers a short walk (starting with a stiff climb) over the small hill of Beinn a' Mhonicag (567m) immediately to the west of the car park, which provides excellent views of the 'roads' and the former site of the lake. The walk described here is easily extended. It is perfectly possible to walk up several of the high points that can be found in and around Glen Roy such as Ben Iaruinn (NN 295 900) at 803m or Leana Mhor (NN 317 879) at 676m. Alternatively, you could undertake a round of the hills at the northern end of the valley including Carn Dearg (NN 357 948) and Carn Dearg Beag (NN 365 941).

Glen Roy

Photo w11.1 |

The parallel roads are clearly visible running along the lower flanks of Glen Roy.

From the car park, enjoy the views up into the valley of the 'parallel roads' (see Photo w11.1) and then head straight up the hill, due west. You will soon pass the lowest parallel road at about 260m height and, after another climb, the second at about 325m. These are quite distinct and fairly broad levels, though somewhat sloping in profile. Carry on upwards for about 25m or so to reach the level of the highest 'road'.

There is no broad ledge at the height of 350m, because the highest 'road' ends just about this point. Similarly, if you turn round and view the opposite side of Glen Roy, the 350m 'road' peters out just north of the plantation on the northern side of Gleann Glas Dhoire (at about NN 309 848). The lower 'roads' do curl around the side valley, however.

At about the 350m contour, you are standing just where the first and highest lake would have butted up against the glacier extending up into Glen Roy from the Great Glen and Glen Spean. It takes some effort of the imagination to conjure up a vision of a lake ending just in front of you with a great wall of ice towering above on the right.

Continue steeply up the rough vegetation for another 200m of ascent to reach the summit plateau of Beinn a' Mhonicag. You should arrive at the 550m contour line, which marks the edge of the summit plateau, somewhat south of the summit cairn. Rather than heading directly to the cairn, it is best to devise a wider sweep southwest for the best views over to the Grey Corries and the Aonach ridge in the distance. More panoramic views can be enjoyed at the summit cairn.

Head just east of north from the summit cairn to start the descent of the northern end of the hill. As you head roughly north and the summit plateau ends, enjoy the increasingly more compelling views of Glen Roy and the parallel roads – this is probably the best place to gain an overview of the valley. It is difficult to imagine what the view in front of you 12,500 years ago would have been like. There would have been a view of a great lake in the valley (see Photos w11.2 and w11.3) and massive glaciers to your south.

You can also see Glen Gloy to the northwest from the summit and on your descent, where sections of the 'roads' in that valley can be noted running along the valley side.

The slope becomes steeper as the ridge drops down in rocky steps, and you will have to move around a bit from left to right and back again to find the line of least difficulty (avoiding craggy corners and bog). Take care to avoid the more substantial crags on the right (east).

After the steepest step you arrive at the top 'road' at about 350m. Bear right onto the road and almost immediately pick up a minor track that descends, under the lowering crags above you on the right, on a falling traverse to the middle 'road' at about 326m and then to the lowest 'road' at about 260m. Following the 'road' from here is not easy, as it lies within a bowl under the crags and the lakeside remains have been eroded more than in other places.

Once you have arrived directly above the parking place, descend on the same track as you used for the ascent to arrive at the start point.

Photo w11.1
Glen Roy today.

Photo w11.3
The same view
towards the end
of the ice age.

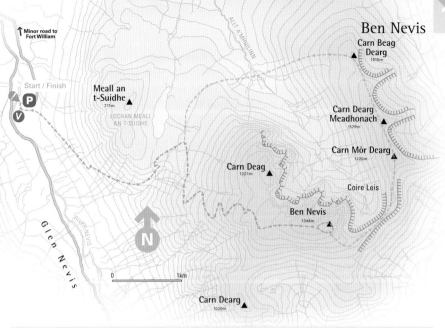

Walk #12
Ben Nevis

START	▶	NN 122 730
FINISH	●	NN 122 730
TIME	◔	6 HOURS+
GRADE	◯	NAVIGATION ● ● ● ● ●
	◒	TERRAIN ● ● ● ● ●
	✦	SEVERITY ● ● ● ● ●

At 1344m, Ben Nevis is the highest mountain not just in the Scottish Highlands but in the whole of Britain. This makes it a very popular place, and the summit area and the main track are often pretty crowded. The views to be enjoyed on the way up and down and from the summit are however appropriately glorious (weather permitting).

From Glen Nevis it is hard to get a grasp of the size of the Ben Nevis massif, even

Ben Nevis

though you can see almost to the top. For a good perspective you really need to put a little distance between you and the mountain. A good view of the whole massif is gained from low ground north of Fort William, for example from near Corpach. The best views of Ben Nevis are from Aonach Mor/Aonach Beag (see Photo 9.1), where the full height of the majestic mountain can be appreciated. For a closer look, the Càrn Mor Dearg arête offers intimate views of Ben Nevis's fearsome northern crags.

While it may be necessary to stand off to get an overview, there is however no alternative to climbing the great Ben if you want to appreciate the detail of its geology and structure. Ben Nevis is a great lump of intrusive igneous granite, topped by a mass of lava of a type known as 'andesite' (which as the name suggests is common in the Andes). The geological story of how these rocks came to form the present-day mountain is outlined in Chapter 9.

Essentially, the collision of an oceanic plate and a continental plate led to subduction of the oceanic plate. This in turn led to the eruption of masses of andesitic lava, followed by two great successive impulses of molten magma squeezed in between layers of existing rock deep underground. The overlying ground, consisting of mainly solidified andesitic lava, then collapsed into the still partially molten mass before forcing its way down into the magma (which then slowly cooled to form granite).

Millions of years of erosion have now uncovered the rocks we see today, with a lower girdle of granite and an upper cap of andesite. The granite girdle extends beyond Ben Nevis to include Càrn Mor Dearg and Aonach Mor to the north.

This walk allows you to see the different rock types and some of the features they exhibit, as well as appreciate some superb views of major tectonic folds in surrounding mountain ranges (especially the Mamores to the south and the Grey Corries to the east).

The recommended walk makes use of the main track from Glen Nevis. The walk is not difficult, but it is something of slog given the height to be gained. This track seems to attract discouraging comments from many guidebook writers, some of whom consider it 'boring' or 'tedious'. I can't agree that any route on Britain's highest mountain deserves such a label. I suspect that the real gripe is that this is a pretty easy route (except for certain potential difficulties as mentioned below), and thus attracts lots of 'tourists'. If you can cope with the number of walkers then this is a super route with stunning views and great geology.

An alternative route for walkers is to use the spectacular Càrn Mor Dearg arête route. This route adds another few hundred metres of ascent and involves a short section of narrow ridge walking, which may not suit everyone, and leaves little time to appreciate the geology. If you are not put off by the extra effort required, it is the best hillwalking route on the mountain.

A few words of warning are necessary. The great height of Ben Nevis means that the weather can frequently be bad. Ben Nevis will often have its summit bathed in cloud even when the surrounding tops are clear. Remember that the length of the walk and its height mean that you could very easily encounter harsh conditions which you may have to endure for some hours, even if you set out in balmy weather. The summit area is often blanketed with snow well into early summer.

Following the main track from Glen Nevis to the summit and back is pretty straightforward. But navigation off the summit in poor visibility, and especially with deep lying snow, can be tricky. If there is no snow on the ground at the summit, it is fairly easy to follow the great number of cairns marking the main route. If there is deep lying snow which hides the cairns and it is misty, then it is recommended that great care is taken until you are clearly on the zigzag track off the summit plateau.

A dog-leg route is essential for safely finding the descent path from the summit cairn area. From the summit cairn follow bearing 233 degrees for 150m, then follow bearing 283 degrees to bring you to the start of the main track. This one potential difficulty is why the navigation for the walk is rated as level 5. Following the track in clear weather would only merit a rating of level 2 for navigation.

Take great care in snowy conditions if you are tempted to go up to the edge of the great drop to the north – snow 'cornices' build up here overhanging the crags, and can easily collapse if you walk out onto them. Stay well back from the edge under such conditions.

I have rated the terrain as level 5, the most difficult. This is because of the difficulty underfoot if there is snow on the summit area; otherwise, the consistently stony track would get a level 3 rating. The severity rating of 5 reflects the fact that if things go wrong evacuation may be difficult. Don't be put off by these words of caution. Tens of thousands of people climb up Ben Nevis every year with very, very few accidents. A few simple precautions and an awareness of the potential dangers will help you avoid any mishaps. Well-prepared parties seldom get into difficulties.

Ben Nevis

Begin at the visitor centre and car park in Glen Nevis, crossing the footbridge in the north-western corner of the car park. Follow the track for a short distance alongside the river then turn left to head up to the start of the long ascent. There are few rock outcrops to be seen initially because of the dense vegetation, but almost from the start there are increasingly impressive views of the glacial trench of Glen Nevis and of the surrounding mountains.

The first rocks seen will likely be grey granite, an intrusive rock created from the first impulse of molten magma underground. Once it was emplaced, this first impulse of magma cooled slowly to form the Ben Nevis Outer Granite. Almost immediately after emplacement, the outer ring was subjected to the injection of more magma into 'joints' created as the first impulse magma cooled and shrunk very slightly. These injections or intrusions form what geologists call 'dykes' or upright sheets of cooled magma that were squeezed between other rocks.

Some of these dykes can be seen as you ascend the first set of zigzags, shortly after the path from the Youth Hostel joins the main track (at about NN 133 720). Look out for a band of slightly darker rock cutting across the grey granite. Photo w12.1 shows a small dark red intrusion about 30cm across cutting through granite.

Photo w12.1 | Dark red igneous intrusion cutting through Ben Nevis Outer Granite (width of view 1m).

Photo w12.2 | 'Onion skin' weathering of 60 million year old basaltic intrusion (width of view 0.75m).

You will also encounter a quite different type of rock in another intrusion encountered between two aluminium bridges crossed on this section. This dyke is rather bigger, being a couple of metres across. This is a much younger rock and is formed of a different type of magma known as 'basalt'. It is an offshoot of the mass of volcanic eruptions that accompanied the opening of the Atlantic Ocean some 60 million years ago (see Chapter 10), which created the rocks of places such as Skye, Mull and Ardnamurchan. This fairly 'recent' basalt intrusion is easily noticed as it is distinctive in colour (its dominant hue is a rusty brown) and from the way it weathers, shedding bulbous layers (see Photo w12.2). This is known as 'onion skin' weathering.

As you gain more height, the track turns off the flank of Glen Nevis to enter a valley cut into the upper part of the slope. Follow the track up into the bealach between Ben Nevis and Meall an t-Suidhe to its north, heading towards Lochan Meall an t-Suidhe. This is a glacial breaching point as the valley glacier coming out of Glen Nevis sent a lobe out across here. The glacier scoured out the shallow basin holding the lochan.

The track turns sharp right at about NN 147 724. Missing this turning is a potential navigational error that could be made on the route up (or more likely going down), but this is not likely in clear conditions. About 500m after turning right, the track begins to turn into a valley and crosses the Red Burn. The pinkish tinge of the granite at this halfway point (being about 675m high) is quite clear here. The appropriately named Red Burn highlights where you pass from the grey Outer Granite into the reddish/pinkish Ben Nevis Inner Granite, at about 450–500m. This was formed by a second impulse of magma being intruded under the ground in the middle of the first impulse.

Geologists work out which granite was intruded first because the intrusive dykes passed earlier on are found only in the Outer Granite and cut right across it. There are no dykes in the Inner Granite, despite sitting in the centre of the combined mass. Geologists therefore conclude that the Outer Granite was intruded first, followed by the dykes and then by the Inner Granite (and much, much later by the 'onion skin' dyke).

The reddish colour suggests that this Inner Granite was subject to more pervasive 'hydrothermal alteration' (from super-hot water containing dissolved minerals being forced up into cooling and shrinking joints in the granite) than the grey Outer Granite.

The Red Burn (Allt na h-Urchaire, to give it its Gaelic name) is a major feature on this side of Ben Nevis, forming a single continuous stream from about 1100m straight down to Glen Nevis at just above sea level. The burn is particularly impressive from the couple of short zigzags between the 500m and 550m contours, where the boulder field that covers the summit of Ben Nevis can be seen higher up the burn.

Ben Nevis

The track now begins to zigzag several times as it takes you up towards the summit plateau. At about the 900m contour (near the zigzag at about NN 151 713), you cross from granite to andesite lava and also enter the great boulder field that will (unless veiled by snow) accompany you all the way to the summit (see Photo w12.3). When you see broken bits of the andesite with a 'fresh face' it will be quite dark, but most of what you will see is a grey rock broken into well-weathered and heavily lichen-covered boulders. All the same, the lichen-covered surfaces are clearly different from the granite outcrops seen so far.

As you tramp up the plentiful zigzags it is worth keeping an eye out for a special sort of andesite boulder known as 'breccia', a rock which contains lumps of rock (see Photos w12.4

Photo w12.3

The andesite lava boulder field capping Ben Nevis with granite below, looking towards Fort William.

Photo w12.4 | Andesitic breccia on the side of the track near the summit plateau of Ben Nevis.

and 9.2). Igneous breccia is sometimes the result of an explosive volcanic eruption ripping apart solidified magma and lumps of the surrounding mountain. Alternatively, igneous breccia can be created when molten lava which flowed out onto the surface of the earth had semi-solidified and was subjected to some form of force (for example, from an earthquake or landslide), causing it to break into lumps. Whatever its origin, the lumps are easily distinguished in some of the boulders either forming the track or at its sides.

As you ascend further, the zigzags become noticeably less steep. This is the signal that you are beginning to near the end of the steep ascent as you get closer to the summit plateau, but there is still some way to go.

The track crosses the great boulder field, the product of freeze-thaw action of water which has seeped into any tiny crack in the rock. Water expands very slightly upon freezing and, if this process is repeated time and again, the rock will eventually be broken up into boulders. You will have plenty of time and opportunity (absence of snow permitting) to contemplate the even longer periods of time involved in this slow breaking up of the mountain.

Eventually you will reach the summit area. If there is no snow on the ground, the first impression is of the great number of old buildings that litter the highest point on the summit plateau. The second impression (absence of cloud permitting) will be the wider scenery. It would be fruitless to describe all the mountains that can be seen from the summit plateau, but it is worth mentioning some key scenic/geological features.

The first wide view is likely to be of Càrn Mor Dearg to the northwest and, beyond it, Aonach Mor and Aonach Beag (see Photo w12.5). The first two of these hills are both part of the Ben Nevis granites. Càrn Mor Dearg is part of the Inner Granite and Aonach Mor part of the Outer Granite (and, as such, is cut across by igneous dykes such as those seen early on in this walk). Aonach Beag is part of a different rock formation, being mainly metamorphic Dalradian schist.

Photo w12.5

Càrn Mor Dearg arête (Inner Granite) lower centre left, Aonach Mor (Outer Granite) upper centre left, linked by dip to Aonach Beag (Dalradian schist) centre right with steeply dipping strata clearly visible centre right.

Ben Nevis

The Grey Corries range beyond the Aonachs is also formed of quartzite. These were the rocks that existed before the Ben Nevis andesites were erupted onto them and the Ben Nevis granites intruded into them. The hills to the south, forming the range known as the Mamores, are also Dalradian rocks (mainly schist and quartzite). The Grey Corries and the Mamores display very impressive large-scale deformation of the quartzite.

It is worth walking away from the immediate summit area to get better views of these surrounding hills. The best viewpoint is the eastern end of the summit plateau overlooking Coire Leis and Càrn Mor Dearg, as there is a sharp end to the plateau. If there is snow around, take very great care to ensure you are not walking onto any cornices by mistake. In good weather, it is worth looping clockwise back around to the main summit on the southern flank of the summit area on, for example, the 1330m contour.

If there is cloud surrounding the summit depriving you of views, take solace in looking closely at the rock boulders all around you. You may well see breccias in the heavily weathered rocks, especially if you've already 'got your eye in' by spotting such rocks on the ascent. A closer look at the rocks might also reveal another feature of lava known as flow-banding (see Photo w12.6). This is a record in the rock of the repeated flows of the lava as the magma was erupted over time. You may even see boulders of 'brecciated flow-banding' where the flow-banded lava has been broken up into lumps, probably as a result of semi-solidified lava being subjected to some external pressure.

When you've enjoyed studying the views and/or the rocks or when the cold starts to get to you, it is time to start the long descent. In the mist (especially when there is snow) take great care to ensure that you take the correct route to the top of the zigzags. The geological study can end here, as you may want to reserve your energy and effort for the descent. Enjoy the views as you pick your way down Britain's highest mountain.

Photo w12.6

Flow-banding in andesitic lava, summit area Ben Nevis.

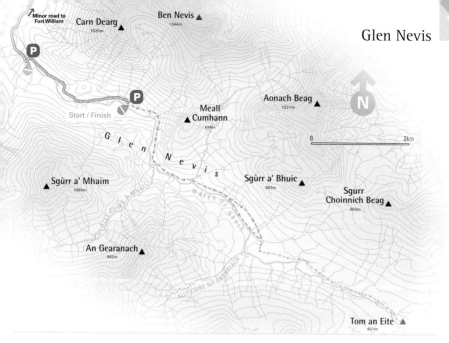

Walk #13

Glen Nevis

START	▶	NN 167 691
FINISH	●	NN 167 691
TIME	◔	2–3 HOURS
GRADE	⊙	NAVIGATION ●
	☁	TERRAIN ● ●
	✷	SEVERITY ● ●

Fittingly, Britain's highest mountain Ben Nevis looms over one of the finest mountain valleys – Glen Nevis. Many visitors to Ben Nevis do not venture further along the valley than necessary to get to the track up Ben Nevis. Glen Nevis is well worth exploring further, however, especially on one of the many days when the mountain tops are shrouded in cloud. The valley has three main parts with very different characteristics.

Glen Nevis

This walk explores the two upper sections of the valley containing an impressive waterfall, a substantial gorge and striking large-scale tilting and folding of rocks, as well as plenty of different rock types and glacial features.

The walk is fairly straightforward with no real difficulties in terms of navigation or terrain, and hazards are limited. The only difficulty some might find is the short sections of stony track in the gorge section. There is very little ascent/descent involved in the walk. After very heavy rain, some parts of the upper section of the valley (just before and after the waterfall) may be impassable except by keeping up on the valley side.

You can shorten the walk by going only as far as the impressive An Steall waterfall or, if you prefer a longer trip, you can wander along the valley as far as you please.

The recommendation is to walk at least as far beyond the Steall ruins as needed to see the great folds in the quartzite on Sgurr a' Mhaim. The view of the folds improves the further you walk, and is at its best just before it becomes hidden by the lower flanks of the Mamores range. You will see tilted rocks near the waterfall but the folds on Sgurr a' Mhaim are a much more impressive sight, conveying an impression of the very powerful tectonic forces that were involved in tilting and deforming the rocks on such a scale.

The drive, bus journey (buses run from Fort William to the last bus stop at NN 146 683, about 2.5km short of the start point), cycle or walk down the first part of Glen Nevis to the starting point is not without geological interest. Glen Nevis's lower section from Fort William to just short of the walk start point is a classic U-shaped glacial valley. The deep channel was carved by a substantial 'valley' glacier (see Chapter 11) fed at different times by corrie glaciers on Ben Nevis and the Mamores. The valley turns sharply left at Polldubh (where the bus turns round), running east–west rather than north–south. The valley also narrows significantly here, although it retains its general U-shaped profile. Another hanging valley stands well above the parking place at the start of the walk, marked by the top of a waterfall or waterslide coming down the steep valley flank over the bare rock.

Follow the stony track from the end of the car park towards Steall. Keep an eye on the rock outcrops in and beside the track and the boulders on the track. Several outcrops and boulders display a conspicuous layering, sometimes as small-scale folds (see Photo w13.1). These are Dalradian schists, tough metamorphic rocks which form Meall Cumhann.

Photo w13.1 | Deformation folds in metamorphic Dalradian schist seen on the Glen Nevis track.

Photo w13.2 | Granite intrusion into Dalradian schist, Glen Nevis track (intrusion is about 5cm across).

Keep an eye out for igneous dykes running across the track in a few places, ranging from a few centimetres to a few metres wide (see Photo w13.2). These dykes have sometimes been exploited by streams, and you have to cross a couple of them.

After about 400m, the river does a very sudden 90-degree right-hand turn. This may not be noticed as you are shrouded deep within a forested area and views are restricted. Shortly after the right-hand turn however, there are a couple of spots where you can see back down the valley with the stream way below you.

In this section of the valley the U-shaped profile has been replaced by a V-shaped valley/gorge. Again, this is not entirely obvious unless you keep an eye on your surroundings and observe upwards as well as downwards. The valley sides close in quite dramatically and you can usually hear the stream thundering down a series of (unfortunately) out-of-sight waterfalls.

The burn then rises to just below the track when you are in a particularly narrow section of what is by now definitely a gorge. The stream is still largely invisible, despite being so close, and is largely hidden by a jumble of large boulders which have collapsed from the higher crags (see Photo w13.3).

Glen Nevis

The burn at the base of the gorge is largely hidden from view by fallen boulders, some of which have been used by the burn to carve out the circular potholes visible on the far side of the gorge.

You can see large circular potholes at the base of the crags where current erosion is taking place. Rocks and boulders carried by flood conditions at this pinch point undermine the crags, eventually leading to further collapse of the crags. If you look up the crags you will see the remains of scooped-out areas rising up for some distance, until vegetation screens the rocks from view. As these hollows are always created at the base of the crags, you are looking at evidence of the progressive lowering of the base of the crags and thus of the stream – evidence of how the gorge was progressively carved downwards.

Immediately after the choke point the valley widens out and the woodland is replaced by open country. The waterfall known as An Steall (which means 'waterfall') comes into view ahead. The best view of the waterfall is a bit further on where the valley performs another 90-degree turn in its course, this time to the left.

The tilt of the rocks in the outcrop to the immediate left of the waterfall is quite clear, trending from upper left to lower right (see Photo w13.4). Indeed, the same pattern is easily distinguishable in the next mountain spur along the valley where folds can also be seen. The water crashes down 70m or so, crossing the tilted rocks where they meet a higher spur.

Photo w13.4 |

An Steall waterfall crossing highly tilted rocks dipping to the right, with folds visible on upper-left background ridge.

From the 90-degree left-hand bend the valley becomes wider. Sloping sides rise up from the flat valley floor to the mountain tops on either side, Aonach Beag to the left (north) and the Mamores to the right (south). Keep an eye out up to the left, as quite soon a near-vertical sweep of tilted rocks can be seen way up on the mountain. The vertical tilt bends towards the upper part of the outcrop, which is more of the quartzite.

Pick a track along the flat valley floor keeping fairly close to the valley side, heading towards a wooden footbridge just before the ruins at Steall. Remember to look back now and again after crossing the footbridge, looking southwest to see the tilted and folded strata below the summit of Sgurr a' Mhaim. As the view improves you can see the spectacular folding of the tilted rocks (see Photo w13.5). In the photo the summit of Sgurr a' Mhaim is slightly below the apparent summit; the upper pointed top is in fact Stob Ban. On the left side of the mountain the tilt is from upper left to lower right, but almost directly below the summit area the rocks bend into a near-vertical tilt. Just to the right of the summit the rocks have been folded into a wavy section.

Photo w13.5 |

Large-scale deformation of quartzite on Sgurr a' Mhaim.

Compare the view to the deformation folds seen in some of the outcrops and boulders of schist earlier in the walk on a scale of a few centimetres. On Sgurr a' Mhaim the biggest fold has a wavelength of several tens of metres or more. Remember that we are only seeing a small part of the overall original rock mass and fold (which took place deep underground). Erosion has removed the overlying rocks and the rest of the folded quartzite.

The high point along the valley, dividing Glen Nevis from the Abhainn Bath valley, is 401m high on Tom na Eite about 8–9km from the start point of the walk. Tom na Eite is a fine viewpoint, but if you don't want to walk that far you could aim for the prominence Tom a' Choinneachaidh (338m) at NN 206 685. This prominence forms an extension of the schist that makes up the eastern side of Meall a' Bhuirich, and can be an atmospheric viewpoint (see Photo w13.6) even in rather damp conditions.

Glen Nevis

The burn is diverted from its general east–west direction by the prominence and flows through a small gorge, an indication that the drainage pattern has been altered. The burn originally flowed in east–west direction to the north of the small prominence. At some point, perhaps when the much bigger gorge seen earlier in the walk was being carved into the rock, the burn was deepened and the burn draining northwards from the Mamores (Allt Coire a' Bhinnein) became the main course for a short section. The main flow was then diverted to the south of the prominence.

On the return leg enjoy the views up to the dramatically folded rocks of Sgurr a' Mhaim, considered by many to be some of the most impressive large-scale rock folds in the Britain. If you used the valleyside track on the way out, then use the narrow track running close to the burn on the way back – it takes you close to the bottom of the waterfall, An Steall.

From near the waterfall you begin to get views of the mountainsides closing in on the valley at the mouth of the gorge. If the weather is reasonably clear you also get some good views of part of Ben Nevis, including the glacial corrie/hanging valley whose outlet burn creates the waterslide at the start of the walk. Return to the start through the gorge and wooded section of the track.

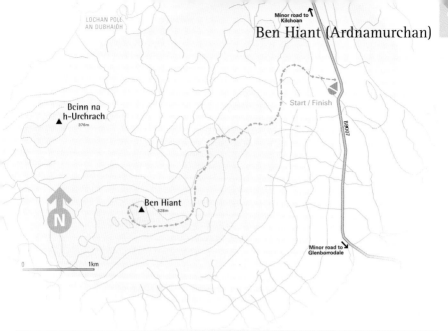

Walk #14

Ben Hiant (Ardnamurchan)

START	▶	NM 551 641
FINISH	●	NM 551 641
TIME	⏱	1–2 HOURS
GRADE	⚲	NAVIGATION ● ●
	⛰	TERRAIN ● ● ●
	⊗	SEVERITY ● ●

The approach to the western end of Ardnamurchan by road is a long one, twisting and turning on a seemingly endless track. The journey is made longer by a big loop inland and then back out to the peninsula's southern coast. The diversion is necessitated by Ben Hiant, a small shapely hill that presents an impassably steep and craggy flank to the coast between Ardslignish (NM 566 614) and Kilchoan (NM 488 637).

Ben Hiant (Ardnamurchan)

Ben Hiant is rather like a layer cake. The base (on the eastern side at least) is lava, erupted onto the surface during the early phase of the volcanic episode which accompanied the opening of the Atlantic Ocean about 60 million years ago. The upper part of the hill is made up of intrusive igneous rock which was emplaced in the latter part of the episode, along with the great volcanic ring complex of western Ardnamurchan (see Chapter 10 and Walk 15). This layering is clear when looking at Ben Hiant from the viewpoint on the approach road at Clach Chiarain (NM 562 616; see Photo 10.4). The recommended route takes you up to the summit over a couple of large steps, represented by crags and/or steeper ground.

The summit of Ben Hiant offers stunning views, especially of Mull to the south. What will interest those with an eye for geology and scenery, however, will be the view of the great igneous ring complex to the northwest. Ben Hiant is 528m high, but the road reaches 170m on its eastern flank giving a short and fairly easy walk up to the summit. It should take little more than about 45 minutes to follow the fairly clear track to the top and the same time to return.

Photo w14.1

Lava flow forming sharp steep slope.

Photo w14.2

Intrusive dolerite sill on the western flank of Ben Hiant.

Ben Hiant (Ardnamurchan)

There is a short vehicle track which runs east from the road at the highest point at about NM 551 641. A short distance up the track there is space to park a couple of cars. Return to the road and pick up the start of a track heading west on the opposite side, which climbs up the hillside. Ahead you can see a sharp steepening of the mainly vegetation-covered slope with some outcrops running off to the left (south). The steeper slope is part of the 'basaltic' lava flow (see Photo w14.1). Metamorphic rocks lie below the lava, also out of sight under vegetation.

A short climb up the steep section takes you onto the top of the first part of the lava and gentler slopes. From here you can see the steep edge to a higher level running off to the west. This level is made up of the intrusive rocks of the 'igneous ring complex', and the recommended route will soon rise up to this level.

Note the intrusive sheet ('dyke') of dolerite running roughly north–south at this point (see Photo w14.2). This is one of several sills on the eastern and south-eastern flank of the Ardnamurchan volcanic ring complex (with a few wider areas on the northern edge). These sills were intruded around the same time as the 'cone sheets' of the ring complex (see Chapter 10).

The track (not shown on OS 1:50,000 map) now trends roughly south-southwest rising gently up a ridge across more of the early lava flow. The rock only changes when the ridge again starts to steepen and narrow at around NM 5432 6370. Here the rocks change from lava to intrusive quartz-dolerite (the name given to mainly dolerite rock with high levels of quartz). The same rocks form the hill from here up to the summit.

The way looks impassable to the summit because of the steep crags facing you as you approach the summit hump from the east. However, the track avoids the crags and heads along under the southern flank of the summit hump, then leads you up to the summit from the south-western side. The summit views are truly fine indeed. The most immediately attractive aspect is south and southeast to Mull and the Sound of Mull, but make sure that you appreciate the full panorama.

The rocks making up the northern part of Mull are from the same lava flows that also form the lower parts of Ben Hiant and the land to its east. This patch of knobbly ground to the east seems less immediately commanding, but it is worth studying the low indented plateau around Beinn Bhuidhe (NM 570 631). The landscape of this area is similar to the flattish ledge below you on the lower flank of Ben Hiant. The linear indentations running northwest–southeast across this area show the individual lava flows from successive eruptions (see Photo 10.2).

Turning north, the area around and beyond Beinn nan Losgann (NM 535 655) is a complex mix of lava and 'cone sheets' from the first phase of the ring complex (see Diagram w14.1 in which some of the larger cone sheets are highlighted). The landscape to the north of Beinn nan

Ben Hiant (Ardnamurchan)

Losgann contains several such cone sheets (four fairly wide and about a dozen narrower ones). These can be seen as low lines of prominences forming small sharp bumps on the horizon. The cone sheets are mixed with Dalradian schists and form the lower ground.

Turning westward, the view is now over the igneous ring complex. The nearest hill is Beinn an Leathaid, which is yet another cone sheet from the second phase of the ring complex (see Photo 14.3). The cone sheet outcrop is over 500m wide. The group of hills beyond Beinn an Leathaid is part of the most complete of the ring cone sheets known as the 'Great Eucrite', eucrite being a form of gabbro (which is what these hills are made of). The high points are Meall nan Con (northwest; see Walk 15) and Meall nan Tarmachan (west-northwest), but it is possible to discern that these tops are part of an almost-complete ring of hills. This ring is the product of the third phase of the ring complex. The group of hills in the far south-western end of the peninsula are cone sheets from the second phase, and form the partial remains of a ring in this area.

Return to the start point by following the inward route, taking care to find the track below the summit of Ben Hiant to avoid the steep crags on the summit's eastern face.

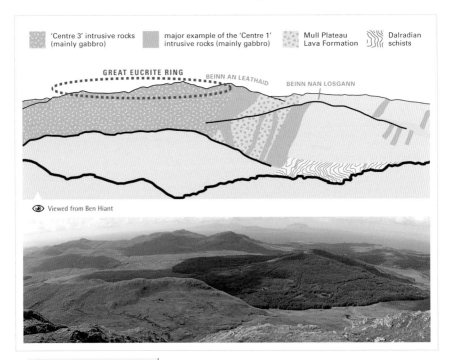

Photo w14.3 + Diagram w14.1 | The volcanic landscape of Ardnamurchan.

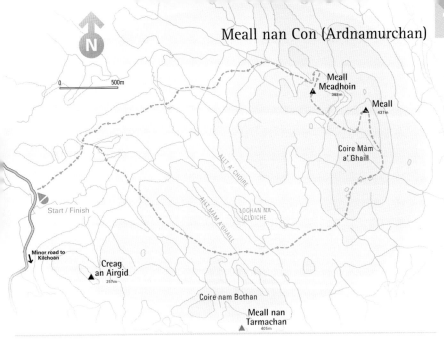

Walk #15

Meall nan Con (Ardnamurchan)

START	▶	NM 473 674
FINISH	●	NM 473 674
TIME	🕒	4 HOURS+
GRADE		NAVIGATION ● ● ● ● ●
		TERRAIN ● ● ●
		SEVERITY ● ● ● ●

The western tip of the Ardnamurchan peninsula is the most westerly point on the British mainland. From a casual glance at a map it appears as an island; Mull lies to its south, Tiree and Coll to its west and Eigg, Rum and Skye to its north. Geologically speaking the peninsula has much in common with Mull, Rum and Skye and also with smaller islands of Staffa, St Kilda, Arran, Ailsa Craig and Rockall.

Meall nan Con (Ardnamurchan)

The rocks of these islands and of Ardnamurchan were created between 60 and 55 million years ago, when vast quantities of magma were created which either flowed out on the surface as lava or cooled down below the surface as intrusive rock. This great outburst of volcanic activity was caused by the splitting apart of a great continental tectonic plate and the creation of the Atlantic Ocean (see Chapter 10). Prior to this gargantuan event, the ancient continental plates of Avalonia (proto-Europe) and Laurentia (proto-north America) had been joined in a single plate with other continents to form a supercontinent known as Pangea.

The chunks of plate or 'terrancs' making up northern Britain and northern Ireland were parked on the edge of Laurentia, while those of southern Britain and southern Ireland were accumulating on the edge of Avalonia. When the continents split apart, however, Scotland and northern Ireland were disconnected from Laurentia and remained attached to Avalonia, becoming part of northwest Europe.

The geological history of Ardnamurchan is covered in more detail in Chapter 10. A key part of that story is the creation of the great volcanic 'ring complex'. Excellent views of the ring complex can be seen from the air; this mode of observation is not very practical for the hillwalker, however. A good ground-based view is available from Ben Hiant (Walk 14) and this walk, Meall nan Con. The ring of hills is quite evident from the OS 1:25,000 and 1:50,000 maps and from aerial photos.

This walk provides a close-up view, taking you right into the heart of the best surviving of the three rings of volcanic hills where the scale of the eruptions is evident. Geology guidebooks usually recommend a fairly easy walk to Beinn na Seilig (NM 456 641), ideal for a good general overview.

The route recommended here is rather more strenuous, but much more rewarding. Careful navigation is required, and the route is recommended only to those with some experience in map reading and use of a compass. The terrain is not exceptionally difficult, but it is very intricate. If you are unsure, take the easier option of a trudge up Beinn na Seilig. If however you have the necessary navigational skills, go for it; the route is a pure delight in a little-walked area. If you meet anyone it will almost certainly be a geologist or an archaeologist! The area is best avoided in the mist as, given the complex nature of the terrain, the navigation would be quite demanding. Use of the OS 1:25,000 map is recommended for this walk, as the necessary detail is not evident on the 1:50,000 map.

The recommended route involves a lot of up and down, in and around innumerable crags and small hills. The effort is repaid with a highly atmospheric exploration of this fascinating landscape.

As you trek around this charming walk, remember that the rocks of Ardnamurchan are youngsters at 'only' 60 million years of age. The ancient gneisses of the northwest of Scotland are 50 times as old (having been created up to 3 billion years ago). Of course, even 60 million years is much too great a period for us to grasp. This walk however gives you a few hours in which the implications of these enormous geological timespans can be tossed around in your brain, as you pick your way through these well-weathered but comparatively youthful outcrops.

Follow the track from the big stile, keeping right at the first fork (after about 200m). Carry on along the track, keeping below a low line of hills on your left (i.e. north) until the track splits again at about NM 478 678. The left track, which is worth exploring for a few metres, bends left into a small, narrow cleft between the small hills. There is a nice view down to the sea through the defile.

Turning left into the narrow defile, you'll see some rock outcrops with easily visible large grains; this is a rock known as 'gabbro' (see Photo 10.3), a name familiar to those who have explored the Skye's Cuillin ridge. The Skye and the Ardnamurchan gabbro outcrops were created by molten magma generated deep within the earth's crust as an ancient continental plate split apart, opening up the Atlantic Ocean.

The molten magma rose through the earth's crust, but did not reach the surface. Instead it cooled slowly below the surface, giving time for the crystals which formed as the magma solidified to grow quite large. The magma was of a type known as 'basaltic'. If this type of magma is erupted on the surface it cools down quite quickly, forming a rock with very small crystals called basalt. Basaltic magma which doesn't reach the surface cools down more slowly and is called dolerite if it is medium grain size and gabbro if it has large crystals. The original magma is identical, but the cooling time determines the grain or crystal size and thus the name of the rock (see Diagram 8.1).

Gabbro is very common in the Ardnamurchan ring complex; almost all of the rocks seen today in the western part of the peninsula are gabbro (except on and around the summit of Meall nan Con). Basalt lava is found on and to the east of Ben Hiant (see Walk 14).

Meall nan Con (Ardnamurchan)

Having taken a look at the outcrops in the defile, turn round to face the way you took to enter the defile, but take the left track (rather than the one on which you entered the defile). Follow the track below a small rise to the left to the stream, to cross at about NM 4805 6779.

Initially follow a small track which rises towards a gap between two prominences on the skyline. Head somewhat to the right of the right-hand prominence into a rising narrow defile, starting at around NM 4821 6758. This defile is quite clear on the OS 1:25,000 map, but is hardly evident on the 1:50,000 map where it is the gap between two sets of four staple-like crag markings. Follow the track up roughly southeast with the small stream on your right, until it peters out. The track gets less and less distinct as it leads you round the back of the prominence on your left, where the higher ground becomes less steep. Bear left before you meet the ridge coming down from Meall nan Tarmachan, and cross that ridge at about NM 490 670.

From here, head towards the low prominence of spot height 311m (NM 498 668). Start heading roughly east to the base of the southern ridge, then follow the ridge north to spot height 403m (NM 5019 6741). After about 30–40m of ascent up this ridge, the rock type changes from gabbro to dolerite, a medium-grained basaltic rock.

This dolerite is possibly the 'roof' or top of the intrusion. The magma at the top, being in contact with the cold pre-existing rocks into which the magma was intruded, cooled more quickly (forming dolerite) than the lower-lying magma (which resulted in the gabbro).

The dolerite stretches northwards for about 2km from this point in a narrow arc about 300m wide, forming a distinct curving ridge. Follow the blunt, bumpy ridge along to the summit cairn on Meall nan Con, the highest point in the Ardnamurchan ring complex. This is a superb viewpoint. Your attention is first drawn to the islands (Rum and Eigg are the closest) and then the distant Highlands which form a jagged fringe to the landward horizon.

When you've soaked up the glorious distant panorama, turn your attention to the hills around you to observe the ring or, as is evident from here, rings of hills that mark the funnel-like sheets of molten magma that rose through the earth (see Chapter 10). The most complete ring is known to geologists as the 'Great Eucrite', eucrite being a form of gabbro. It was created by the third and last of three massive 'central type' volcanoes which form the conical ring shapes of sheets of intrusive igneous rock.

The terrain within the Great Eucrite ring is more subdued, although there are inner rings. The centre of the volcanic ring structure, just east of Achnaha, is very low relief and quite unexciting compared to the wider rings generated by the same volcano. There are far fewer remains of the first and second episodes. However, Meall Meadhoin is one of about ten small patches of gabbro from the very first episode found within the Great Eucrite of the third episode.

Meall nan Con (Ardnamurchan)

Photo w15.1

Meall an Con: dolerite upper left, gabbro right.

An outer ring is seen to the east and northeast, forming the line of hills from Beinn an Leathaid (NM 517 676) running roughly north to Meall nan Fiasgan near Fascadale on the northern coast. This line of hills is lower than the Great Eucrite and less rocky, but is a key remnant of the first 'central type' volcano.

Despite being only 437m high, the views from Meall nan Con are worthy of a much higher mountain. You will feel the urge to linger and enjoy the vast open scenery with its mix of hill, sea and island. When ready to leave, the next objective is Meall Meadhoin which is about 400m to just north of west. It is not practical to get there in a straight line, however, and the routing from here becomes quite intricate. So make yourself aware as best you can of the complex interplay of ridge and dip.

Return to the slight col about 200m south of the summit where a small lochan (NM 502 679) sits at the head of Coire Màm a' Ghaill (the OS 1:25,000 map places this name some way to the south of the lochan). This diversion is necessary to avoid the crags on the northwest face of Meall nan Con which bar the direct route. Keep well to the east of the lochan, making your way right around the base of the crags and up to a minor col. Cross the col heading towards Meall Meadhoin and then turn round to look at the crags beneath the summit of Meall nan Con (see Photo w15.1). The different colours of the two rock types, gabbro and dolerite, are clearly seen in the rock face.

Make your way up the ridge towards spot height 388m, the summit of Meall Meadhoin. Cross the short distance to the lower spot height of 374m (not marked as spot height on OS 1:50,000 map) at about NM 4966 6823. You should notice that the rock here is distinctly rougher than that around the 388m spot height. The rocks are part of the first episode (not of the third and final episode) around the 374m spot height.

Meall nan Con (Ardnamurchan)

There are in fact a dozen or more small patches of rock from the first phase which crop out in the Great Eucrite ring. The patch here is an egg-shaped area, only about 250m east–west and 100m north–south (the 374m spot height lies on the northeast edge of the outcrop). The rocks to the left (west) are a light grey with lots of white lichen, while the rocks on the right (east) have less white lichen and display a brownish tinge.

There are also superb views from this vantage point (see Photo w15.1). From here you can see the centre of the third great episode as well as the ring structure – most notably of the Great Eucrite's lower hills – fringing the northern coast (see Photo w15.2).

The challenge now is to work out a route back to the start point. Your objective about 3km to the west is fairly clear, but as soon as you try to head towards it you are diverted by interlocking spurs. These spurs guide you, forcing you to head in the wrong direction for some distance. As you enter the valleys between the spurs you also lose sight of where you are going, so a good sense of direction is handy as is close observation of the map.

The immediate objective is to get to the head of a steep gully/valley at about NM 4945 6800 in an atmospheric rock bowl. Make your way down on the right-hand side of the stream, picking up traces of track here and there at the base of the crags on your right. You get good views of the centre of the third episode as well as sea views beyond as you descend. The track may be tenuous, but the scenery decidedly magnificent.

At the bottom of the rocky section of the gully, cross the stream avoiding heading further down the gully. Head roughly west across rising ground at the inner base of the Great Eucrite hills. A prominent gully/valley comes into view on the left after a while. Follow minor tracks, passing near spot height 125m at NM 482 681, to rejoin the outward track just near the small defile met on the outward journey where there were some gabbro outcrops (at about NM 4784 6716).

Photo w15.2 | The Great Eucrite ring, looking north from Meall Meadhoin.

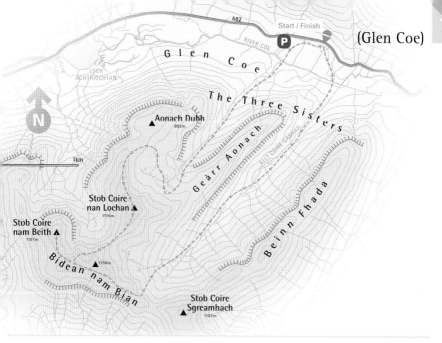

Walk #16
Bidean nam Bian (Glen Coe)

START	▶	NN 171 568
FINISH	●	NN 171 568
TIME	⏱	6 HOURS+
GRADE	⌂	NAVIGATION ● ● ● ○
	⛰	TERRAIN ● ● ● ● ●
	⚡	SEVERITY ● ● ● ●

Glencoe is one of Scotland's most renowned historical as well as scenic locations. The long drive, cycle or walk down Glen Coe is certainly one of the most memorable highland journeys you can make anywhere in Britain, but the real drama is found by leaving the glen and heading up the hills.

To the north, the lower slopes of Aonach Eagach give no hint of the vertiginous

Bidean nam Bian (Glen Coe)

route that awaits those who attempt to traverse the knobbly ridge from east to west. All attention is directed instead to the fearful buttresses of the southern side of the great trench of Glen Coe. The mountain appears unassailable to mere walkers.

However, as long as you can cope with steepish stony tracks and the ascent via 'The Lost Valley', the walk along the Bidean nam Bian ridge and the descent via Coire nan Lochan is demanding but not difficult (these words obviously do not apply in bad weather conditions). On Bidean nam Bian there is none of the exposed scrambling demanded on the Aonach Eagach ridge.

The walk is best avoided in poor weather. One point of navigation needs especial care: the structure of the ridge is rather complex with the Aonach Dubh and Gearr Aonach ridges branching out from Stob Coire nan Lochan, and not from the main ridge at Bidean nam Bian. The excess of detailing of rock outcrops on the OS 1:25,000 map makes it difficult to picture the structure of the ridges unless you study the map carefully. The structure of the ridge is much clearer on the OS 1:50,000 map.

For those interested in geology, this area offers more than compelling scenery. The dramatic landscape is the product of the interplay of very violent volcanic eruptions, irresistible mountain-building forces and intense glacial erosion. This walk takes you into the very heart of an area of glacially sculpted volcanic rocks.

Glen Coe is relatively well served in terms of geological publications with a special 1:25,000 geological map and a book to accompany the map (*Glencoe Caldera Volcano, Scotland* written in the standard academic geology style), both published by the British Geological Society.

The walk begins and ends at the busy car-parking place opposite the Three Sisters of Glencoe. The spot is often adorned with a kilted piper serenading the coach parties of passing tourists, who are only permitted a five-minute glimpse of this stunning spot.

It is worth spending a little time here to appreciate the stark, steep flanks of the Three Sisters, the three great rocky buttresses (from left to right in Photo 9.3) Beinn Fhada, Gearr Aonach and Aonach Dubh, separated by the two deep clefts of Coire Gabhail (the 'Lost Valley') and Coire nan Lochan.

The buttresses are well vegetated in their lower reaches, but clearly layered rock outcrops are prominent in the upper slopes. The layering is especially clear on Aonach Dubh in Photo

9.3 where layers tilted slightly down to the left poke through the vegetation. These lower layers are 'sills' (formed by sheets of cooled magma that cooled between existing rock). The upper layers are 'pyroclastic' rocks where the magma has exploded into fragments, large and small, instead of flowing as a fluid mass as with lava. The walk will head up into Coire Gabhair, passing through pyroclastic rocks until near the ridge when the route passes into rock that originated as lava. More pyroclastic rocks are encountered on the descent.

Before starting take note of the course of the stream below you, running in a shallow gorge. The stream has been cut into an intrusion, a dyke running northwest–southeast. This is a comparatively 'recent' intrusion dating from the Carboniferous period (about 300 million years ago), whereas the majority of the igneous rocks around here date from some 400 million years ago. Indeed, in addition to the lavas and pyroclastic rocks, there is also a 'swarm' of dykes dating from 400 million years ago which run southwest–northeast. Several of these dykes will be seen on the recommended route.

From the car parking area, drop down to pick up the track heading to a footbridge over the burn at about NN 173 563. Climb steeply up from the bridge. Some way up you come to what looks like a cave on the left, but this is in fact simply a gap between large fallen boulders. Continue up the track through an increasingly impressive rock fall until you meet a very large tumbled boulder barring the way. Ford the burn here and pick up the track on the other side.

Eventually you emerge quite suddenly from the narrow confines into a wide shallow valley floor enclosed by steep mountain slopes on either side. This is the 'Lost Valley', hidden from below by a substantial rock fall from high up Gearr Aonach on the north-western side of the valley. This rock fall has blocked the valley so that material carried down by streams from further up towards the ridge has built up behind the rock fall. This all becomes more apparent as you rise up on the track towards the ridge.

Photo w16.1

Welded tuff.

Bidean nam Bian (Glen Coe)

As you start to ascend the track at the end of the wide valley floor, the rocks on either side are pyroclastic rocks known as 'tuffs' and 'breccias' (depending on the size of the fragments of magma at the time of the eruption). A common pyroclastic rock in the area is known as a 'welded tuff' (sometimes called an 'ignimbrite'). It can be distinguished by the streaks formed from pumice ripped away in a very violent eruption, then flattened and welded into the main fabric of the rock when it was deposited (see Photo w16.1). The eruptions creating welded tuffs are the hottest and most violent known and the burning cloud of incandescent gas, magma and ripped-away lumps acts like a fluid, sometimes leaving traces of flow patterns in the rocks (see Photo 9.4). There were seven great cycles of these super-hot caldera-creating eruptions in the Glen Coe area, each enlarging the depression or 'caldera' formed when the land slumped down following the eruptions.

Further up the valley you pass into rocks that originated as true flowing lava, of a type known as 'andesitic'. The transition is at about NN 155 543 and is made more complex by the presence of a couple of southwest–northeast-trending dykes, running roughly parallel to the direction of the track. Reddish rocks can be seen in the track and around when you cross the dykes.

The track gets steeper as you near the ridge. You may see some examples of 'columnar jointing' in the andesite (see Photo w16.2). Columnar jointing is the same as ordinary jointing in rocks, created in igneous rocks when they cool down and contract very slightly. Under the right cooling conditions, the joints are created in a more-or-less regular pattern which often resembles columns. The best-known examples are around Fingal's Cave on Staffa and at the Giant's Causeway in Northern Ireland. The examples seen on this walk do not match these classic outcrops, but are clearly columnar in structure and are formed in exactly the same way. You will pass crags displaying columnar jointing later on the recommended route.

Photo w16.2 |

Columnar jointing

in andesitic rock.

Bidean nam Bian (Glen Coe)

On reaching the ridge you are rewarded with entrancing views. If you have the energy, the views can be improved further by ascending another 130m to the top of Stob Coire Sgreamhach (but remember there's still some way to go, and plenty of good views to come).

To continue the recommended route, head northwest along the wide ridge towards the summit of Bidean nam Bian. Keep an eye out for dykes as you cross them (identifiable from the reddish rocks). Also note the small glacial corrie high on the ridge below the col between Bidean nam Bian and Stob Coire nan Lochan.

It doesn't take long to reach the summit at 1141m. Bidean nam Bian is the highest mountain top in the Glencoe area and there are pretty magnificent views to be had in clear weather. It is well worth the walking the extra 500m to the north-western high point of Stob Coire nan Beith, as you are rewarded with fine views over the northern end of the ridge (see Photo w16.3). This short diversion also offers some very good views of the dykes cutting across the ridge between Bidean nam Bian and Stob Coire nan Lochan as well as bringing you close to some outcrops of the reddish dyke rock (see Photo w16.4).

Photo w16.3 | View southwest from Bidean nam Bian. Note the granitic dyke cutting across the ridge (near the upper snow patch), leading to Stob Coire nan Beith,

Photo w16.4 | Granitic dykes crossing either side of the summit of Stob Coire nan Lochan, seen from Stob Coire nan Beith.

Bidean nam Bian (Glen Coe)

Return to the summit of Bidean nam Bian and plan the route to Stob Coire nan Lochan. This is where a possible confusion may arise if the topography is not fully appreciated. It is necessary to cross over to Stob Coire nan Lochan before descending into any valley to follow the recommended route.

Descend from Bidean nam Bian to the col between it and Stob Coire nan Lochan. The small glacial corrie mentioned earlier is clearly seen below to the right (southeast) where there is a collection of small lochans. This corrie would still have been able to sustain a small glacier even when the temperature was not cold enough to support glaciers at lower heights, such as towards the end of the last ice age.

The wide reddish dyke that crosses the ridge up to the summit of Stob Coire nan Lochan (see Photo w16.4) is clearly seen cutting across from left to right at an angle to the line of the ridge. You then cross the dyke as you ascend to the summit and more superb views.

To descend, keep to the northern ridge of Stob Coire nan Lochan. The slope is nowhere as steep as you might expect and the way down opens up additional views as you descend. The main point of geological interest is the regular columnar jointing in the rock outcrops.

Follow outcrop after outcrop of columnar jointing (see Photos w16.5 and w16.6) down to the bealach with its tiny lochan at NN 1501 5572. The columnar jointing forms a 'pavement' in places, and the column 'tops' can be seen in plan. The section view of the long columns is seen in the crags. Freeze-thaw mechanisms work on these joints allowing erosive forces to seep into the deep recesses of the rock face, helping to break it up into blocks or boulders.

Photo w16.5 | Looking back up at the columnar jointing on the crags of Stob Coire nan Lochan.

Photo w16.6 | The tops of columnar jointing exposed as a pavement on the ridge.

Bidean nam Bian (Glen Coe)

About 150m before reaching the tiny lochan, the rocks change to a pinkish breccia. This is a pyroclastic rock containing visible lumps (strictly speaking the lumps should be over 64mm in size but, in practice, the term is used for clearly visible lumps). These are large fragments of solidified magma and bits of the existing rocks that were ripped away in explosive pyroclastic eruptions, cemented together by smaller fragments of volcanic 'ash'. They are pink, purple, grey and blue in colour and are heavily coated in lichen, but the lumps are quite visible (see Photo 9.5).

From the bealach you can head down towards three lochans in the wide glacial corrie at the head of Coire nan Lochan and pick up a good track which descends on the eastern side of the lochans. Alternatively you can aim for a gully which eventually carries a stream (at about NN 1522 5556) down which you descend very steeply, eventually meeting and crossing the burn descending from the three lochans then turning left on meeting the track. This more direct (but more hazardous) route gives good views of the waterfall as the burn crosses the lip of the corrie.

The rest of the descent through Coire nan Lochan is a wonderful walk beside a staircase of small waterfalls. The falls effectively merge into a single continuous cascade as the valley drops steeply from 650m to 200m over a distance of about 1.3km. The flanks of Gearr Aonach and Aonach Dubh rise up on either side of this narrow glacial valley which was carved out on the line of a cluster of intrusive igneous dykes. These dykes provided the weakness along which the ice could do its destructive work.

As you descend, you pass under a series of crags on your right (southeast) bringing you close to a variety of rocks and features including breccias, flow-banding, reddish granite, light-coloured rhyolite and darker andesite.

During the descent, the path passes an exposed slab of rock sloping steeply down towards the burn. The track itself bears left towards the burn just before this slab (indeed it is the first time that you are brought down close to the burn). The interesting feature about this slab is the set of shallow parallel lines that run across it at roughly 90 degrees to the angle of the slope of the slab. These are 'glacial striations' caused by rock fragments embedded in a glacier, scraping the bedrock as the glacier flowed over it (see Photo w16.7). The striations are very shallow and are not seen on many rocks, despite the fact that glaciers passed over all the bedrock around here and scratched it extensively.

So what happened to all those other striations? The answer lies in the very shallowness of striations. Over roughly 10,000 years since the glaciers retreated, chemical weathering of the exposed surface of the bedrock has been sufficient to remove the rock down to below the

Bidean nam Bian (Glen Coe)

depth of the striations. However, where vegetation rapidly covers the bedrock surface, the rock is protected from atmospheric chemical weathering and striations are preserved. It is therefore most common to see striations where bedrock has only recently been exposed, most often by the action of booted feet rubbing away vegetation.

Many people have heard of striations and often assume that any mark in the rock is an example, particularly jointing in rocks (caused by slight contraction on cooling and/or drying when first laid down). This exposure of striations next to the track shows you what to look for: shallow, straight parallel lines in recently exposed rock. A couple of joints can be seen crossing the striations at different angles.

The only awkward sections of the descent follow just below this point, where a couple of sloping slabs have to be crossed. The track then stays up fairly high before directing you down to a footbridge and a track back to the start point, where you will have another chance to enjoy the view of the Three Sisters.

Photo w16.7

Glacial striations or scratches made as the glacier passed over this rock surface 10,000 years ago, seen running up from the bottom to the top of the photo across the wet outcrop (width of view 3m).

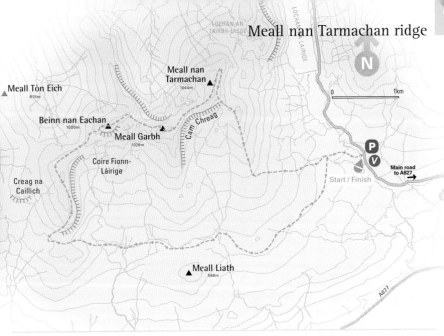

Walk #17

Meall nan Tarmachan ridge

START	NN 609 379
FINISH	NN 609 379
TIME	5 HOURS+
GRADE	NAVIGATION ● ● ●
	TERRAIN ● ● ● ●
	SEVERITY ● ● ● ●

Meall nan Tarmachan and three linked tops of Meall Garbh, Beinn nan Eachan and Creag na Caillich form an intricate, twisting ridge line that offers superb walking among fantastic scenery, with fascinating geological interest.

The rock outcrops on the ridge walk clearly display the 'plastic deformation' undergone when these metamorphic rocks were compressed during the collision

Meall nan Tarmachan ridge

of continental tectonic plates. The deformation is visible on different scales. On the mega-scale, the overall tilt of the rocks forming the whole mountain mass (and also the wider range) is quite evident. The layering of the rocks on this large scale determines the general shape or grain of the whole mountain surrounding the ridge. Smaller-scale deformation zones are also easily seen within the overall picture, indicating how the rocks reacted to the great pressures to which they were exposed.

The walk also passes a very clear and substantial igneous intrusion which forms steep cliffs. The different scenery produced by the two types of rock is obvious on the walk.

Although three of the tops are 1000m or so high, the amount of ascent involved in the walk is reduced by the fact that the starting point is also quite high at 500m.

The ridge has two short-lived challenges for those who don't enjoy steep slopes. The route from the very conspicuous summit of Meall Garbh heading for Beinnn nan Eachan involves a short section along a narrow ridge. This is then followed by an unpleasant section of descent across sloping rock faces. It is only a short section and is not particularly steep; it looks rather fearsome from above, however. There is an alternative, easy route of descent via the south ridge from Meall Garbh which cuts the walk length by about half.

The summit point of Meall Garbh also looks fairly fearsome when first seen in detail from the summit of Meall nan Tarmachan. It is much less worrying when you get closer to it, however, and its peculiar shape means it is well worth a visit even if you don't do the full walk. If you don't fancy walking up to the summit point, the alternative route on the south ridge starts from below the final climb to the summit.

Cross the road and the stile over the electric fence directly opposite the car park entrance. The track along the first couple of hundred metres was only just coming into use at the time of my last visit, and was something of a boggy mess. Cross the stile and drop down to a burn, cross it and rise up the other side to meet another stile. Cross a boggy section until you meet a new, well-made track. Turn right and follow this well-made track until it joins a wide vehicle track at about NN 603 379.

Take the small track on the opposite side of the vehicle track, marked by a small inconspicuous cairn. The small track heads just south of east, climbing steadily through the hummocky terrain until eventually you pass some abandoned metalwork from the hydroelectric scheme. You can see a fence coming into view on the left and then a track coming up from the lower part of the southern ridge. Your track then swings sharp right to rise steadily up the ridge (at about NN 591 377).

Quite soon you reach spot height 923m (NN 589 385) and its very fine views. The dam at the southern end of the Lochan na Lairige reservoir comes into view here. Water is collected from all over this side of the mountain to add to intake for the reservoir, as will be seen later in the walk.

A short drop follows, crossing a muddy patch before rising up to cross a low hump. This brings you to the base of the summit crags, rising quite steeply at one point. When the track reaches the base of the crags it bears towards the northern end of the summit plateau, passing under the crags that guard the direct route and rising gently.

Turn round at some point below the summit plateau to view the way you have come. The prominences reflect the way erosion has worked at weaknesses in the layers of rock, which are tilted roughly towards you here. This layered effect, with slight prominences with a lower area behind them, is a common theme of the mountain landscape to be seen throughout the walk.

The track eventually curves round, taking you to the summit plateau little more than 100m to the north of the summit cairn. Views open out immediately as you arrive on the plateau, encompassing the ridge towards Meall Garbh and its nib-shaped summit point.

The walk from the summit of Meall nan Tarmachan to that of Meall Garbh (about 1km southwest) is very straightforward on a knobbly, broad ridge. Keep an eye on the rock outcrops underfoot as you make your way towards Meall Garbh for excellent examples of small-scale deformation folds. You can also try to discern a much larger pattern as you walk along here, with rock layers clearly tilting from upper right to lower left.

In some places you can see both large- and small-scale deformation in the same outcrops. Photos w17.1 and w17.1 show layers of rock tilting from lower right to upper left. On the lower left of the outcrop, small-scale folds in the rocks can be seen within the layer of tilted rocks. The overall tilt is evidence of massive deformation folds to geologists, who map wide areas and seek accounts that explain the pattern of outcrops. Large-scale deformation folding clearly plays a significant part in explaining the mad mosaics to be seen on geology maps. The Grampian Highlands were subject to considerable 'plastic deformation' during metamorphosis caused by continental collision, and these tilted rocks represent parts of the major 'antiforms' and 'synforms' and even overturned folds or 'nappes' (see Chapter 7).

Meall nan Tarmachan ridge

Photo w17.1 | The larger scene shows the overall tilt from lower right to upper left, representing large-scale deformation folding of the rocks.

Photo w17.2 | A small section of the crag with severe small-scale deformation folds.

Just before reaching the conspicuous summit of Meall Garbh, a track leads off left down the southern ridge. This is a good descent route for those who want to cut the walk short and/ or avoid the narrow and steepish sections just after the summit on the recommended route.

The summit of Meall Garbh is fairly narrow, but nowhere as fearful as it looks from afar. The track takes you round the south side of the angled tip of the summit, rather than its more precipitous northern side. The tip makes a good shelter (if the wind is coming from the right direction) where you can sit and enjoy the scenery, including the view of the narrow ridge walk to follow. This summit point may be 20m lower than that of Meall nan Tarmachan, but it is the better viewpoint (see Photo w17.3).

The narrow section of the ridge is very short, with the grassy sides soon becoming less steep. If you can cope with the steep slopes, stop midway across the crest of the ridge and look back towards the summit point. Severe deformation of the rocks can be seen in outcrops just below the summit point (see Photo w17.4).

The track then takes you to the top of a short descent across some tilted rocks that look rather intimidating. This is perhaps not the best of times to divert attention away from the task of ensuring a safe descent, but this section does bring you in close contact with the overall tilt of the rocks. Careful placement of feet and a steadying hand are key.

After this unpleasant section, an easier descent takes you to a steep-sided bealach. This is probably either a glacial 'meltwater channel' carved down into the rock by powerful glacial streams (perhaps running underneath a very large glacier) or a glacial breaching point where ice flowed across from one side of the ridge to the other.

Meall nan Tarmachan ridge

On the walk from below Meall Garbh to the summit ridge of Beinn nan Eachan, keep an eye out for the characteristically hummocky terrain below the northern side of the ridge between Meall Garbh and Meall nan Tarmachan. These are not 'hummocky moraines' (material deposited by glaciers), but ribs of bedrock which have been eroded by glaciers along weaknesses between layers within the rock. This glacial erosion exposes the 'grain' of the rocks and, on close examination, it is clear that the hummocks are well ordered in lines; this is another example of the way in which the tilted rocks define the shape of the hillsides.

The climb up to the summit of Beinn nan Eachan is straightforward, passing through layers of rock. Some of the schist to be found underfoot and in outcrops is so shiny that it is reminiscent of the two-tone material that has been in and (mercifully) out of fashion several times over recent decades. It is most shiny when freshly broken off an outcrop; weathering lessens the sparkle but it can still be distinguished (especially on a sunny day).

Photo w17.3 | View west along the narrow section of the Meall Garbh summit ridge with Beinn nan Eachan centre middle distance and Creag na Caillich left middle distance. The knobbly terrain typifies the Grampian scenery in this area.

Photo w17.4 | Deformation folds just below the summit of Meall Garbh.

Meall nan Tarmachan ridge

At the last short rise before the summit of Beinn nan Eachan you can clearly see the tilt of the rocks and again an example of a small-scale deformation within the tilted rocks.

When you've descended from the summit to the bealach, look back across the southern face of Beinn nan Eachan to see the complex structure of the slope with its shelves with their up-tilted edges (see Photo w17.5). This is another example of how the overall shape of the mountain is heavily influenced by the tilted layers of rock.

The track across Creag na Caillich is rather precipitous where it curves around the eastern side at the top of crags. This section can be missed by leaving the track and heading directly over the top, but the vertiginous route along the edge offers better views.

The track down from Creag na Caillich seems to want to take you in the wrong direction, trending increasingly westwards. When the track nears the bealach however it swings round the base of the crags in an easterly direction to the top of a broad gully. The reason for the diversion becomes apparent as you approach the gully. The problem is a substantial crag that runs up towards the summit of Creag na Caillich. The rock is significantly different to the schist we have seen so far on this walk: it looks much cleaner, lacking the vegetation and variety of lichen that camouflage the schists. Most impressive however are the flat surfaces, marked only by random jointing.

These rocks are an igneous intrusion made from a magma intermediate between rhyolitic and basaltic composition. As you descend the gully you will see how extensive the dyke is and how it runs across the corrie, forming a prominent feature (see photos w17.6 and w17.7).

The head of the gully is at about NN 564 367. The track leads down to a small dam at the end of the track marked on the OS 1:50,000 map at NN 567 367. What looks like a track is actually a leat (artificial watercourse); the actual track is discernible a bit lower down.

The dam and the leat are part of a system used to divert the streams around here into the reservoir. From here a pipe contours round the hillside, mainly out of sight, collecting more water at each burn. The system has its advantages but the little valleys below the water capture level are rather sad-looking affairs, bereft of the water that has carved them out. The absence of water, however, exposes the rocks to geologists and hillwalkers. Just below the first dam you can see rocks with clear horizontal tilt, then vertical and then horizontal again, showing how the rocks broke up under the pressures of continental collision of tectonic plates, undergoing 'brittle' deformation into cracks as well as 'plastic' deformation into folds.

Follow the hydro-scheme track past several water capture points and one short stretch of exposed pipeline crossing a small dip, until the track joins a vehicle track. Turn right and follow it back, enjoying the fine views of Loch Tay and Ben Lawers, to the point where you joined the vehicle track on the way out (at NN 603 379). A short distance remains, first via the newly laid track and then the developing muddy track back to the roadside stile opposite the car park.

Photos w17.6 + w17.7 | An intrusive dyke runs across the slopes below Creag na Caillich, forming a steep slope for several hundred metres.

Meall nan Tarmachan ridge

Photos w17.8 | The narrow section on Meall Garbh

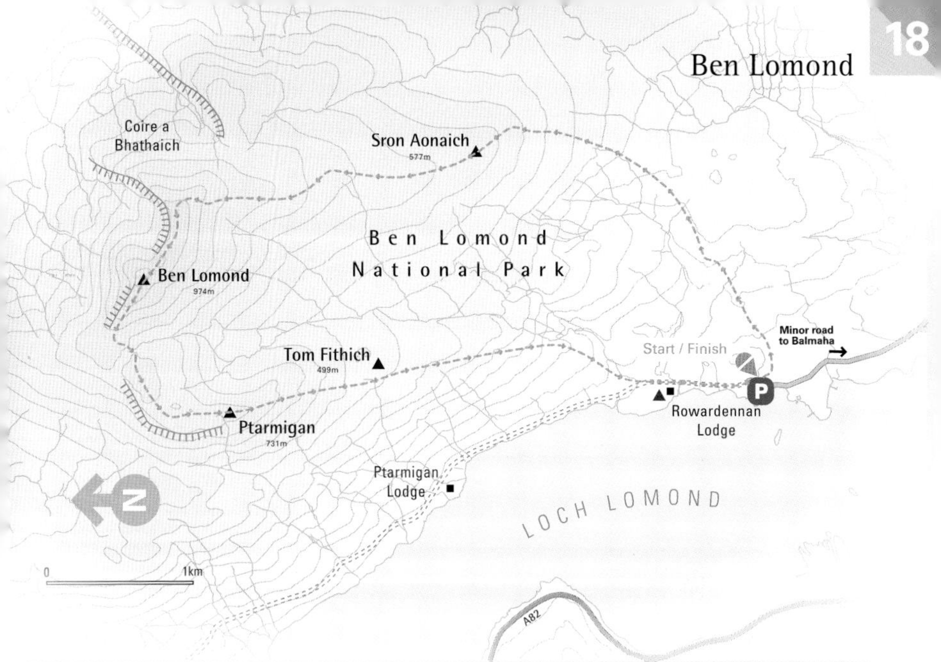

Coire a
Bhathaich

Sron Aonaich
577m

Ben Lomond
National Park

Ben Lomond
974m

Tom Fithich
499m

Start / Finish

Minor road
to Balmaha

Rowardennan
Lodge

Ptarmigan
731m

Ptarmigan
Lodge

LOCH LOMOND

0   1km

A82

Walk #18

Ben Lomond

START	▶	NS 359 986
FINISH	●	NS 359 986
TIME	◐	5 HOURS+
GRADE	⌾	NAVIGATION ● ●
	☁	TERRAIN ● ● ● ●
	❸	SEVERITY ● ● ●

Ben Lomond is a highly popular mountain, its accessibility and stupendous views attracting a steady stream of walkers plodding their way to the top. Some estimates suggest that as many as 30,000 people a year make their way up and down the southernmost of the 'Munros' (as the Scottish mountains higher than 3,000 feet are known).

Ben Lomond

The Highland Boundary Fault (see the Introduction and Chapter 7) cuts emphatically across the southern end of Loch Lomond 10km south of Ben Lomond, marking the boundary between the Highlands and Lowlands. Ben Lomond illustrates how rapidly the mountains of the Highlands achieve grandeur. The views from the summit of Loch Lomond and the 'Arrochar Alps' framed by the wider range of the Grampian Highlands make this a very rewarding walk (if you are lucky enough to enjoy good weather).

Ben Lomond may seem rather unexciting on the geological map of the area, as it's one of those areas where there is no change in the rock colouring on the map. This tells us that the overall rock type doesn't change and that there are few faults, intrusions or other topography-determining features to be found. Once out on the rocky Ptarmigan track, however, this is a tough craggy mountain and the rocks show it.

The Grampians are made up of metamorphic rocks, mainly schist (although there are also substantial outcrops of granite). The whole area has also been crushed by powerful forces generated by the collision of continental tectonic plates, introducing large- and small-scale deformation of the rocks. The rock layers plunge downwards as they approach the Highland Boundary Fault. The fault zone itself is a pile-up of different rock types, some dragged up from the ocean floor during subduction. The Grampian rocks have been severely squeezed, deformed and cracked during continental collision. Glaciation then worked on the rocks to leave the present-day landscape.

Several examples of small-scale deformation zones are seen on the walk, especially on the Ptarmigan track. Some of the best examples of deformation are seen just below the summit.

Since a circular track is generally preferable to a simple out-and-back along the same track, I have described an ascent using the easy and popular tourist track and a return via the spectacular Ptarmigan track. However, I will fully understand if you choose to go up and down on the same track in this special case. Personally, I prefer to use the Ptarmigan track for both legs of the walk as it is much more interesting and rocky than the tourist track. The big advantage in ascending Ben Lomond via the Ptarmigan track is that you get good rocky views ahead of you virtually all the way; likewise, the Ptarmigan track on the descent provides sumptuous views of Loch Lomond. The advantage of an ascent on the main track is that it is an easy plod with no real steep or rocky sections; similarly, wide-ranging views can be enjoyed on the easy descent of the tourist track.

Ben Lomond

Begin from the National Park car park at Rowardennan. Pass through the open centre of the information building to gain the main tourist track which rises gently through woodland for a short distance. You may note one outcrop that you pass which displays a feature known as 'onion skin weathering', where a rock weathers layer by layer in forms derived from jointing in the rock.

You pass into open country at about NS 372 991, gaining views of Loch Lomond. The going gets mildly steeper after the 300m contour, but the pace eases off again above the 500m level with the track rising in the middle of a very broad ridge. By this time the views are beginning to open out quite widely. You will meet more rock outcrops in and around the track, and it is worth keeping an eye out for signs of deformation.

The track steepens and zigzags to climb up the final rise to the summit. If you have the energy, it is worth leaving the track at about the 900m contour to continue up the ridge line and meet the top of the crags of Coire a' Bathaich. The main track stays resolutely below the top and denies the walker some very fine views (but leaving the track for the edge is not a good idea in windy conditions).

The views are overwhelming on reaching the summit, with mountain top after mountain top competing for the attention (see Photo w18.1). Notice that the peaks are all roughly the same height, with no single peak standing high above its neighbours. This is a fairly common facet of the Highlands in general, although the actual level varies from area to area. There is no general agreement on the cause of this feature, although it is often attributed to erosion creating a plain which undergoes later elevation and erosion. This general shared level is also common among young mountain ranges such as the Alps, Andes and Himalayas, so the actual reasons must be sought in the evolving science of plate tectonics and the dynamics of mountain building and destruction.

Photo w18.1

View northwest from the summit of Ben Lomond.

Ben Lomond

Photo w18.2 + 18.3 | Deformation folds in rocks seen on the descent via the Ptarmigan track.

The descent via the Ptarmigan track begins by heading from the summit down the northwest ridge. This is a bit steep in places but presents no great difficulties, although you will need to be careful on the long, stony steps.

Competing with the demands of negotiating the stony descent, your attention will be also be drawn to the views and, hopefully, to the rocks. There are numerous impressive deformation zones to be seen on the descent from just below the summit all the way down along the Ptarmigan. To get the most out of the descent, look around closely at the outcrops (see Photos w18.2 and w18.3).

Once you have dropped down as far as the bealach at about 750m where the track swings southeast, it makes sense to leave the main track and pick your own route along the top of the ridge (you will see more deformation outcrops this way).

The views of Loch Lomond improve steadily as you descend and are at their very best from the end of the Ptarmigan. Loch Lomond is very long with a narrow northern tip and a very wide southern end, almost like a very lanky triangle. Although not visible, the depth of the loch also varies. It is quite deep in its narrow northern stretches and fairly shallow in its broad southern sweep. This is indirectly visible from the group of islands which break the loch surface at its southern end (see Photo w18.4).

The southernmost line of islands shows where the Highland Boundary Fault crosses the loch. The glacier which carved out the valley floor cut down most deeply where it was confined by resistant rocks, but where it met less resistant rock it was able to cut outwards more easily and thus didn't need to cut down deeply. The landscape around the loch reflects this different resistance to erosion, where lower and more rounded hills are found on either side of the lower part of the loch (including the southern reaches of Ben Lomond) and sharply pointed peaks feature from around Ben Lomond northwards.

You'll be led back to the main track by the time you reach spot height 731m. Enjoy the very fine views of Loch Lomond as you follow the track down towards Rowardennan.

Photo w18.4 | The lower reaches of Loch Lomond seen from the descent of Ben Lomond via the Ptarmigan.

Acknowledgements

My thanks for assistance in many ways to James Keele, Jim Langley, Phill George, Lisa George, Steven Roberts, Johnny Dawes, Reg Atherton, Clair Drew, Bill McGann and Mehmet Karatay. Also to Franco Ferrero of Pesda Press for continuing support for the Rock Trails series, to Peter Wood for the books' design and Don Williams of Bute Cartographics for the maps. Reg Atherton, Gordon Simpson and Ian Smith kindly provided some of the photographs.

Bibliography

Bailey E et al, *The Geology of Ben Nevis and Glen Coe*, 1960.

Craig G (ed), *Geology of Scotland,* 1991

Emelus C et al, *The Paleogene Volcanic Districts of Scotland*, 2005

Gillen C, *Geology and Landscapes of Scotland*, 2003

Goodenough K et al, *Exploring the Landscape of Assynt*, 2004

Goodenough K & Krabbendam M (eds), *A Geological Excursion Guide to the North-West Highlands of Scotland*, 2011

Gribble C (ed), *Ardnamurchan: A Guide to Geological Excursions*, 1996

Hernaiz P, *Structural evolution of the Moine Thrust Belt in Northern Assynt (NW Scotland): Balanced cross sections and fault rocks*, 1990 (www.sociedadgeologica.es/archivos/REV/3(1-2)/Art12.pdf)

Johnson M & Parsons I, *Geological Excursion Guide to the Assynt District of Sutherland*, 2000

Johnstone G & Mykura W, *The Northern Highlands of Scotland*, 1989

Karatay M, *Modelling the subglacial hydrology of the Greenland ice sheet*, 2010

Kokelaar B, *Glencoe Caldera Volcano, Scotland*, 2006

Krabbendam et al, *The internal structure of the Moine Nappe Complex and the stratigraphy of the Morar Group in the Fannichs – Beinn Dearg area, NW Highlands*, 2011 (nora.nerc.ac.uk/14107/1/Krabbendam_Fannich_Structure_SJG.pdf)

Lawson T, *Classic Landforms of the Assynt and Coigach Area*, 2002

Open University, *Mountain Building in Scotland*, 2003

Pattison D & Harte B, *The Ballaculish Igneous Complex and Aureole: A Field Guide*, 2001

Roberts J, *The Highland Geology Trail*, 1998

Sissons J, *The Evolution of Scotland's Scenery*, 1967

Stephenson D & Gould D, *The Grampian Highlands*, 1995

Stone P, *Bedrock Geology UK North*, 2008

Strachan R et al, *An Excursion Guide to the Moine Geology of the Northern Highlands of Scotland*, 2010

Thomas C et al, *Geological structure and landscape of the Cairngorm Mountains*, 2004 (www.snh.org.uk/pdfs/publications/commissioned_reports/F00AC103.pdf)

Trewin N (ed), *Geology of Scotland*, 2003

Upton B, *Volcanoes and the Making of Scotland*, 2004

Williams N (ed), *The Birth of Ben Nevis*, 2010

British Geological Survey maps

1:25,000 scale geology maps:

Ardnamurchan Central Complex – up to date and very detailed; plenty of cross-sections.

Glen Coe – up to date and very detailed; plenty of cross-sections.

1:50,000 scale geology maps:

Assynt Special Sheet – detailed, current and very useful; plenty of cross sections.

Exploring the Landscape of Assynt – easy to read and up to date; accompanying booklet available.

S92 [Inverbroom] – 1:63,360 surveyed 1913; covers a large area; no cross-section.

S91 Gairloch – up to date.

S82 Lochcarron – 1:63,360 scale, surveyed 1913; covers a large area; no cross-section.

S74(E) Aviemore - fairly up to date, but no cross-section.

S72(W) Kintail – fairly up to date, but no cross-section.

S72(E) Glen Affric – fairly up to date, but no cross-section.

S71(E) Kyle of Lochalsh – fairly up to date, but no cross-section.

S64(W) Newtownmore – very recent.

S63(W) Glen Roy – up to date.

S62(W) Loch Quoich – fairly up to date, but no cross-section.

S61 Arisaig – 1:63,360 scale, 1967 survey, no cross-section.

S54(W) Blackwater – 1923 survey, no cross-section.

S53 Ben Nevis – 1:63,360 scale, 1921 survey; covers a large area (including Mamores and Glencoe).

S45(E) Dalmally – 1930s surveys with updates.

S38(W) Ben Lomond – 1980s surveys; no cross-section.

1:250,000 scale geology maps:

Sheet 58N 06W Sutherland.

Sheet 57N 06W Great Glen.

Sheet 56N 06W Argyll – all three sheets are useful overviews.

Glossary

Andesite – fine-grained intermediate igneous rock, either 'extrusive' (usually as lava) or 'intrusive'.

Basalt – rock formed from 'basaltic' lava flows.

Basaltic – describes the chemical nature of molten magma as low in silica content (contrasted with rhyolitic which is high in silica content); cools to form 'basalt' if flows onto the surface as lava and as 'dolerite' if it doesn't reach the surface and cools down below ground (forming medium-sized crystals) or 'gabbro' (forming large-size crystals).

Basin – low lying area (usually but not necessarily undersea level) of basement or present day surface. Rivers drain into basins and sediments are dumped in them.

Bedding – common feature of 'sedimentary' rocks, usually indicating a change in the pattern of sedimentation. Very thin bedding is known as 'lamination' (as frequently found in 'shale'). In limestone bedding may represent

Brittle deformation – deformation as a result of cracking of rocks, as opposed to plastic or ductile deformation. Occurs on the surface and up to a depth of about 15km deep.

Calcium carbonate – an insoluble salt occurring in 'limestone' and other rocks; however, dissolves in water containing carbon dioxide.

Deformation – changes in the physical structure of rocks due to immense pressures generated by continental collision; can be 'brittle' deformation or 'plastic' ('ductile') deformation.

Diagenesis – processes affecting sediments at low pressure and low temperature (i.e., on or near the earth's surface) and result in the formation of a mass of solid rock from loose sediments – see 'lithification'.

Dolerite – 'basaltic' intrusive igneous rock (i.e. it did not reach the surface when the molten magma rose up through the crust) and formed medium-sized crystals.

Ductile deformation – see 'plastic deformation'.

Dyke – more or less vertical intrusion of igneous rock

Effusive – eruption of flowing magma to create lava flows and eventually lava rock.

Fault – a crack in bedrock, can be a few centimetres to many kilometres, can be deep or shallow, can be active or passive. Often caused by tectonic activity.

Flaggy sandstones – thinly bedded sandstone which easily splits on bedding.

Fossil – the preserved form of ancient animals or plants or traces left by them. The hard parts are either preserved or replaced by another mineral (such as 'calcite' or quartz). The term is also applied to preserved geological features, eg a fossil sea bed or a fossil cliff.

Gneiss – metamorphic rock, often displaying banding, but does not split easily.

Granite – intrusive rhyolitic rock, large-grain size as it cools slowly deep down.

Grit – a 'sedimentary' rock made from large particles of sand. No longer an accepted term for academic purposes but is too well established to be ignored.

Ignimbrite – 1) hottest and most violent type of pyroclastic eruption; 2) rock created by such eruptions welded tuff)

Imbrication – piling up of thrusted rock sheets.

Lamination – very thin 'bedding' as occurs in 'shale' – see bedding.

Lava – 1) molten magma that flows onto the surface of the earth;
2) rock formed from lava flows

Limestone – a general name for any sedimentary rock containing more than 50 percent calcium carbonate, usually, but not always, derived from animal shells and skeletons. There are many different types of limestone.

Lithification – the process of forming a 'rock' from loose material (eg sand grains) both close to the earth's surface and deeper in the crust (following subsidence, deep burial etc.).

Lithology – name for the general characteristics such as composition and texture of rocks, usually sedimentary rocks but not always.

Lithosphere – the 'sphere of the rocks', combines the crust and outer mantle to form tectonic plates.

Magma – molten rock formed below the earth's surface.

Mantle – the layer of the earth between the crust and the core; divided into the inner mantle and outer mantle with the crust and outer mantle forming the lithosphere or tectonic plates.

Metamorphic – rock formed from another type of rock that has undergone physical, temperature or chemical transformation.

Mineralisation – process where gases and fluids from heated lower layers of the crust pass up through faults and cracks, causing changes to rock and depositing minerals, some of economic value.

Mineral vein – line, usually along a fault, where mineralisation has taken place.

Mudstone – made from mud grains eroded from land and deposited as sediments in a sea or lake or river, then hardening into rock.

Plate tectonics – see 'tectonic plate'.

Plastic deformation – rocks change internal shape as a result of the application of
forces generated by continental collision; takes place from about 10km below the earth's surface.

Pyroclastic – explosive eruption of 'fragments' of magma ; creates 'tuffs' of various sorts.

Quartzite – 1) sandstone made of fairly pure quartz; 2) metamorphosed sandstone with over 80% quartz

Rhyolite – fine-grained rhyolitic igneous rock, can be intrusive or extrusive.

Rhyolitic – magma or rock formed from magma with high proportion of silica; does not flow easily so often cools down in vents and leads to explosive 'pyroclastic' eruptions.

Sandstone – a 'sedimentary' rock made from sand grains eroded from land and deposited as sediments in a sea or lake or river, then hardening into rock.

Schist – metamorphic rock displaying lamination along which it easily splits.

Sedimentary – rocks formed from sediments dumped in seas, lakes and rivers. Limestone, sandstone, shale, etc. are all sedimentary rocks. Other categories of rock are 'igneous' (volcanic) and 'metamorphic'.

Sill – more or less horizontal intrusion of igneous rock.

Sink hole – hole in the surface of limestone into which surface water drains. Also known as swallow hole, swallet, shake hole.

Siltstone – a 'sedimentary rock' made from silt grains eroded from land and deposited as sediments in a sea or lake or river, then hardening into rock.

Slate – low grade metamorphic rock where high pressure, but not high temperature, realigns minerals so that they split easily along a 'cleavage' plane.

Tectonic activity – earthquakes, folding, faulting, thrusting and earth movements (up, down and/or lateral) caused by the interaction of 'tectonic plate' boundaries.

Tectonic plate – the earth's surface is divided into a series of interlocking but independent plates of which there are two types: continental and oceanic. Tectonic plates, or the lithosphere, consist of the earth's outer layer, the crust, and the next inner layer, the outer mantle. There is a discontinuity between the outer mantle and the inner mantle and the plates move around on this discontinuity, propelled by convection currents within the inner mantle.

Terrane – chunk of continental crust with its own geological history; combines with other terranes to form continents.

Thrusting – large-scale, more or less horizontal movement of rocks as a result of pressure generated by colliding continental plates. Occurs in a 'thrust zone' about 10-15 km below the surface, where plastic and brittle deformation both take place.

Tufa – precipitated calcium carbonate deposits

Tuff – rock created by fragmental (pyroclastic) eruption; various forms including air-fall tuffs, ahs-flow tuffs and welded tuffs.

Index to Place Names